DAMN SHOES
AND
OTHER TALKING TALES

DAMN SHOES
AND
OTHER TALKING
TALES

A SELECTION OF TRUE NARRATIVES
ABOUT PEOPLE WHO DIRECTLY AND INDIRECTLY
EXPERIENCE COMMUNICATION DISORDERS

DANIEL R. BOONE, PH. D.

Foreword by Leonard L. LaPointe, Ph.D.
Epilogue by Julie Barkmeier-Kraemer, Ph. D.

Forman Publishing Group

Foreword by Leonard L. Lapointe
Afterword by Julie Barkmeier-Kramer
Edited and Prepared for Publication by Zachary A. Forman

PRINTED IN THE UNITED STATES OF AMERICA

ISBN 978-0-615-28456-9

PRESENTED BY:
FORMAN PUBLISHING GROUP
PO Box 36270
Tucson, Arizona
85740-6270

www.FormanPublishing.com

CONTENTS

DAMN SHOES AND OTHER TALKING TALES

I first ran into Dan Boone at Rose Memorial Hospital in Denver. I was an intern dipping my feet in the pool of clinical experience supervised by Dr. Darrel Teter. Dr. Boone was already one of the big names in our field. He was a voice guru. He was new at the University of Denver and Dr. Teter had invited him to Rose Hospital to meet the staff and present a little introductory lecture. To appreciate how long ago this was by a metric of technological advance, Dr. Boone described an innovative treatment strategy of creating a tape loop by fastening together length of tape and threading it on a reel-to-reel tape recorder (probably a Wollensak). The tape loop could then be used for "ear training" or auditory feedback; providing a continual model of an appropriate pitch level; or many other examples of repetitive stimulation that may be necessary in voice or speech therapy.

He presented these innovative clinical ideas ("focus on 'Can-Do' therapy; don't neglect the things the person still can do.") with a series of ironic and clever comments that cracked me up. I was bowled over and highly amused. Here was a messiah who came from the plains of Kansas with a tongue blade and a tape loop and a sense of humor that rivaled that of George Burns and Bob Newhart. Through the years we became friends (perhaps drawn together by our mutual quirky admiration for those who reside in left field...though he preferred Bob Feller) and it has been my pleasure to associate with him on many occasions through the years.

I remember well his reign as President of the American Speech-Language-Hearing Association (ASHA) in 1976. Jimmy Carter defeated Gerald Ford in the presidential race of the United States; the Montreal Summer Olympics fans watched Nadia Comaneci tumble and swing her way to 10 perfect scores; and people were humming *Take It to the Limit* by the Eagles. America celebrated its bicentennial and ASHA was presided over by red-white-and-blue Daniel R. Boone. Our Houston convention attracted thousands and I had the pleasure of introducing Dr. Boone at the Plenary Session of our national convention. One of the introductory tidbits used in tracing the footpath of Dan Boone's life was "his childhood was uneventful." Well, anyone who knows him realizes the irony in that line. His childhood and his entire life have been anything but uneventful. He has set the standard for clinical service and clinical research and his focus has always been on the humanness of the person with a communication disorder.

Once upon a time, until the Victorian age or so, healers had little in their tool bags except their mercy with which to guide that mysterious thing we call a *therapeutic encounter*: that charged interaction, both emotional and physical, upon which so much depends in healthcare. Now that lab tests and 10-minute physician encounters have replaced house calls and getting to know the personal history of an afflicted person, we rarely come across healthcare viewed through stories. Increasingly, however slowly, the healthcare professions are looking to what has been called "narrative medicine" to help restore the humanity and compassion that in the eyes of many has been lost.

The past few years have seen an upsurge of writing about illness and the illness experience by both healthcare professionals and patients who are trying to restore a sense of worth and empathy in order perhaps to deal with the dehumanizing effects of technological explosion. We can glean a lot from the stories of people with disorders. In medicine, Rita Charon, M.D., Ph.D., is Professor of Clinical Medicine at the College of Physicians and Surgeons of Columbia University and a leader of the emerging field of Narrative Medicine. Charon first coined the term "narrative medicine" in a January 2001 article in the *Annals of Internal Medicine.* She characterizes narrative medicine as healthcare practiced with the narrative competence to recognize, absorb, interpret and be moved by the stories of illness (Charon, 2006).

In ***Damn Shoes and Other Talking Tales***, this brilliant collection of stories of people with communication disorders, Dan Boone incorporates principles of narrative healthcare. His collection of stories is amusing and poignant and is well seasoned with the Boone touch of humor on wry. He pulls together clinical moments that can enlighten anyone who is interested in putting a human face on personal tales of struggle.

REFERENCE

Charon, R. (2006). *Narrative Medicine: Honoring the Stories of Illness.* New York: Oxford University Press.

Leonard L. LaPointe, Ph.D., Francis Eppes Distinguished Professor of Communication Science and Disorders, Program in Neurosciences; Faculty, College of Medicine Florida State University, Tallahassee, FL

PREFACE

IN **Damn Shoes and Other Talking Tales**, we take a fascinating look at many speech pathologies, the people who have them and their effects on their families and the people around them. **Damn Shoes** is the story of a woman with aphasia who could only yell "damn shoes" while yelling in the stadium at a professional football game. All of the brief stories we tell here, anecdotal tales, were true clinical or situational events observed by me in my 58-year career as a speech-language pathologist (SLP). Only occasional names and locations have been changed when viewed necessary to protect patient identification.

I have told these tales to colleagues and students over the years, hopefully illustrating how communication disorders affect the human connection between speaker and listener. Much of our story focus is on how listeners react to the patient's talking difference. We can marvel how one relates to the patients coping with aphasia, or families struggling with their loved one's dementia, or people with voice problems or stuttering who long to speak more like their listeners.

It has been difficult for me to call myself a *speech-language pathologist* (SLP), our official name as designated by our professional organization, the American Speech-Language-Hearing Association (ASHA). As an undergraduate, I was trained to be a *speech therapist*, and on my first professional job in an aphasia clinic in a Veteran's Hospital, I was called a *language retraining instructor*. I have been called a *speech clinician* and when later working with voice patients, I was a *voice clinician*. In the late 1970s my professional designation was *speech patholo-gist*, and in the 1980s, we emerged as *speech-language pathologists,* our professional title to this day. The people with the talking problems for most of those years were called *clients* or *patients*. There exist today, however, more exotic names for designating clinical groups, such as *speech handicapped* or *voice handicapped* or *communicatively impaired* [sic].

My first job experience was helping young men with aphasia, who had experienced devastating head wounds during the Korean War, learn to talk again. It was my first exposure to the problem of aphasia, and the first talking tale in this

volume well describes the positive impact I experienced working with this population. Later in graduate school and after, I was fortunate to work for seven years in
a chronic disease hospital in Cleveland, where I saw people with a stroke-induced
aphasia and met some who struggled to speak and to swallow with degenerative
diseases (like Parkinson's disease or amyotrophic lateral sclerosis.) Later at the
University of Kansas Medical Center, I headed up the speech pathology unit of
a children's rehabilitation center and evaluated children and young adults with
cerebral palsy from throughout the state of Kansas. At the University of Denver
in Colorado, we began an intensive voice clinic for people with any kind of voice
problem, ranging from a child with a cleft palate to a young woman with vocal
nodules causing a hoarse voice, to the severe dysarthria (a motor speech problem}
of an older man with Parkinson's disease.

At the University of Arizona over the years, I headed the clinical program for
children and adults with speech-language-voice problems. I taught such graduate
courses at Arizona as aphasia, voice disorders, and communication problems in
aging. My favorite role there, however, was to "turn on" graduate students to
the wonders of the clinical process. We appreciated the view that to be human
was in great part to be able to speak. How do the patient's listeners react to the
faulty communication? I wanted students to appreciate the pain of the patient's
disability, which was often the shaping force behind the patient's hope eventually
to "talk more like other people." Also, how patients felt about their talking effectiveness after therapy was always part of our study of therapy outcomes.

In 1971, I first published a voice text, *The Voice and Voice Therapy*, which
is now in its eighth edition. The book opened up a world of consultation for me
as it has been published over the years in English, Spanish, Portuguese, Japanese,
Chinese, Korean, and more recently in Arabic. World travel unfortunately
competed with my first love, working with patients. Until my retirement from
the University of Arizona, administrative, research, and teaching duties occupied
most of my working time. I have enjoyed, therefore, the retirement years that
have given me time to work directly again in a small practice in Tucson with a
few people who have trouble talking

In this volume, *Damn Shoes and Other Talking Tales*, I hope to provide
the reader, who may be unfamiliar with speech pathology, a glimpse of speech-
language-voice disorders, and of the people who have them. The focus of many
of these stories is about the impact of the patient's talking problem on their
listeners, who usually expect the speaker to understand and speak the same way

they do. When speakers speak differently than their listeners, some listeners react inappropriately. The difference in talking, like speaking with a stutter, can shape the response of the listener. Or the unexpected verbal response of someone with aphasia (such as the woman who could only say or yell "damn shoes") often forces the listener to give literal meaning to such a repetitive utterance. Or the faulty spoken responses of a man with Parkinson's disease may not be understood by his listeners. Or patients with dementia, who may look like everyone else the same age, may give an unrelated or bizarre response to a stranger's question. Or the woman who has lost her voice cannot make her feelings known on the phone to her son who is somewhere away from home.

The talking tales presented in this volume have been witnessed by me over a fifty-five year clinical career. After recently writing most of them down, I have asked professional colleagues, former patients and their families, and friends of mine to give the tales a read. While many of the tales evoke laughter when they are read, others bring out sadness and tears. Many readers were unaware of the enormous impact that talking problems may have on the people who have them and on their families. To help the reader appreciate the distinct difference between different communication problems, I have grouped the tales according to specific etiologic groups:

Tales of Aphasia: These are true stories about patients who acquired some kind of brain damage from either head trauma or a stroke, leaving them with language problems in understanding (spoken language and reading) and expression (speech and writing.)

Tales of Dementia: A few patients with senile dementia, usually of the Alzheimer's type, are described in various talking situations.

Tales of Neurogenic Disorders: Communication situations are described for a wide variety of neurological-impaired patients (cerebral palsy, Parkinson's disease, head injury, etc.)

Tales of Voice Disorders: The stories of a few voice patients were selected from a large clinical file of children and adults with voice disorders.

Tales of Speech Pathology: We consider three people and their severe problems of stuttering, and we then look back with some amusement at some frustrating problems I encountered in my professional travel over the years.

Daniel R. Boone, Ph.D., Professor Emeritus
Department of Speech, Language, and Hearing Sciences
The University of Arizona, Tucson, AZ

I

TALES OF APHASIA

A distinctive feature of the human being is the use of language, particularly the ability to talk and understand the definitive speech of others. Together with our human spoken language skill is written language, the ability to read and to write. **Aphasia** is characterized as the partial or complete loss of spoken and written language skills, usually the result of an injury to the brain from either head trauma or a vascular stroke. A great portion of my fifty-five year clinical career has been spent as a speech-language pathologist working with adult patients with aphasia.

The type of aphasia the patient has is related to the site and extent of insult to the brain. In general, aphasia develops from lesions to the left cerebral hemisphere (left brain.) The more forwardly positioned brain lesions produce what is known as a **non-fluent** aphasia, characterized by extreme complications in saying words, while retaining fairly good understanding of what others are saying. More posterior brain lesions often produce **fluent** aphasia, in which the patient may speak with a jumbled or jargon speech, often completely unaware of his or her own jargon and also showing some difficulty in understanding the speech of others. Most people with aphasia actually end up performing somewhere in between the extremes of non-fluent and fluent aphasia.

While the type of aphasia is determined by the site of the brain lesion, how well the patient communicates is usually determined by his or her personality and by the reactions of the people surrounding the patient.

All normal speakers speak to express their ideas, their needs, their feelings; patients with aphasia, even with their compromised speech, speak for the same reasons. Our attempt in this chapter is to lead the reader to appreciate the differences and communication struggles of the adult person with aphasia. As we recount some speaking situations and conditions, they may appear humorous and produce laughter. We are not laughing at the patient, but rather at the reactions of the listener who takes literally the patient's verbal responses in particular situations. In a different light, the reader may experience an emotional tear while reading about someone recovering from aphasia. Although most of the aphasia tales occurred dating back to the 1950s, some recent names and locales have been changed when possible to protect patient identity.

We begin with the aphasia tale **The Thank You**, a story that had great impact on me as a clinician over a life-time career as a speech-language pathologist. We then tell the story **Damn Shoes**, a fun example of a non-fluent aphasic woman cheering at a football game. Like many people with non-fluent aphasia, her perseverative responses of the same few words were taken literally by those surrounding her in the stadium. Two other talking tales, **Away** and **Water, Water, Water,** provide an amusing perspective on how the typical listener responds to these repetitions of non-fluent aphasia patients. A retired airline pilot with fluent aphasia describes in his own jargon speech problems he once had landing a DC-10 in **Circling Over Dallas**. In **Your Penchant for Apples?**, the reader will experience some of the frustrations shared by the patient and clinician when attempting to evaluate a patient's newly acquired aphasia. Of the many speech therapy group sessions that I have experienced, we have selected one narrative in particular, **Honolulu Annie**, which illustrates some fun interaction in aphasia group therapy.

APHASIA TALE 1

THE THANK YOU

DURING the Korean War, I worked as a language retraining instructor in the aphasia clinic at the Long Beach Veterans' Hospital in California. The majority of our speech-language patients at that time were young men who had sustained some kind of head injury in the battlefield. One such patient, whom I will always remember, was Louie, a 19-year old Mexican-American who fell in combat while carrying a large Browning automatic rifle. When he fell, he dropped the gun, discharging a bullet through his left eye, destroying much of his left forehead, skull, and the anterior brain behind it. His injury produced a right-sided paralysis (hemiplegia) and a profound non-fluent aphasia. For six months before transferring to our VA hospital, he had been in a service hospital in Japan, unable to utter a single word. When I first saw him, his aphasia was about seven months old.

***

I went to visit him on the aphasia ward for the first time. His chart had noted that he had good comprehension of both English and Spanish, but was unable to speak or write. My quick testing of his ability to read and understand what was spoken revealed good function, confirming the chart notation (which often, with aphasia, assumes falsely that the patient has no problem in understanding.) Louie demonstrated a severe expressive aphasia. When asked to say a simple word like "ball," he could only awkwardly purse his lips and make no sound. He could not successfully follow any of my attempts at showing him how to say a simple word.

On my second visit with Louie, however, he was able to imitate a word. We had practiced humming, which he could do now with some ease. We then looked in a mirror and decided if we were humming and slowly opened our lips, a word like "ma" would come out. I demonstrated this for Louie. He was able to do it and celebrated his success by repeating the word "ma" again and again. Other patients on the ward and his mother (who visited every day) cheerfully joined in our therapy program, encouraging him to continually flaunt his new accomplishment.

Once we had the beginning /m/ sound, I introduced Louie to a spiral bound notebook. On the top of the first page, we wrote in big capital letters the /m/ sound and underneath it, the word "ma." Within a day or so, we had a list of 15 words, all beginning with /m/ that Louie was able to say without much prompting: "ma, mom, morn, man, more, main, me, mean, many, mama, moon, my, may, make, meat." At the bottom of the page were /m/ sentences like "Many men on the moon."

Once one sound had been mastered and Louie could say it on request with very little struggle, we would move on to another sound, such as /p/. Each page in the notebook had the practice words at the top and sentences below them. Over a six month period, Louie and I had developed some 300 words in the notebook which he could say with ease.

When I left the Long Beach VA for graduate school in Ohio, I did not see Louie again until seven years later. He appeared at a national convention on a panel of "recovered aphasic patients." I sat in the audience listening to each one of the people who had recovered from aphasia. I marveled with great pride as Louie, in near normal speech, told his recovery story. At the session break, I got up from my seat and walked towards the speaker's platform. Louie saw me and walked down to greet me (he walked with a cane because of his continued right sided paralysis.) As we met in the aisle, I could see the old worn out spiral bound notebook in his left hand. For a moment, neither of us said anything. Instead, we embraced one another like the long lost friends that we were. Finally, he looked to me and said through his tears, "I just want to thank you for helping me learn to talk again." No thank you ever meant so much to me as that one.

***

Many patients with aphasia can make functional recoveries if they have enough speech-language therapy. Louie received three hours daily of group and individual speech-language therapy for almost two years. Besides his speech and language retraining, he had physical and vocational therapy. His excellent motivation helped him to make the most of his therapeutic opportunities. Despite his one sided paralysis (hemiplegia), loss of one eye, and slight residuals of motor aphasia, he built a wonderful life for himself; he married, had three children, and was employed for many years by McDonnell-Douglas building commercial airplanes until he retired. I always look forward to receiving his annual Christmas card with those same meaningful words, "Thank you."

APHASIA TALE 2

DAMN SHOES

HERE we have the title story of this book, 'Damn Shoes.' The star of this narrative was a 44-year old woman, a WAC veteran of World War II, who was a non-fluent aphasia patient in the Long Beach VA aphasia clinic. She was diagnosed as having "Broca's aphasia" (her predominant problem was the inability to speak.) She became well known in the neurology section of the hospital for her inability to say anything but the perseverative simple phrase "damn shoes." She would repeat the nonsensical phrase with differential inflections. For example, if I asked her if she wanted a home-pass for the coming weekend, she would reply with an enthusiastic "damn shoes," complete with all the happy-voice inflection that would confirm her desire to go home for a few days. If I asked "do you like the coffee on the ward?" her negative voice inflection would say "no" as she repeated "damn shoes." We will call her Mary Lou. She was normal in appearance with no arm or leg weakness, with her only apparent deficit being the severe aphasia that permitted her to say only "damn shoes" with perfectly sounding speech.

One of the more pleasant tasks I had as a young speech-language pathologist at the Long Beach VA in the early 1950s was to accompany our aphasic patients to various recreational programs. The internal programs included visiting with a visiting movie star every other week (Loretta Young, Doris Day, and Kathryn Grayson among others.) Recreational programs outside of the hospital grounds included deep sea fishing, picnics, and various professional athletic events. Another speech clinician and I would accompany about twenty-five patients, most of whom had some form of aphasia, on the bus to an arena, stadium, or other event destination.

Mary Lou frequented these field trips. One Sunday afternoon, we visited the Los Angeles Coliseum with tickets for row 35 near the forty-yard line to see the Los Angeles Rams against the Chicago Bears. The game was billed "A battle between Bob Waterfield of the Rams and Sid Luckman of the Bears." Mary Lou was a real Rams fan and thus, stood up and hollered loudly for every Ram advance and opportunity. The problem was that all she hollered was "damn shoes!" Throughout the first quarter, I watched as the people seated in the rows ahead continually looked back to see who it was that kept yelling "damn shoes" on nearly every play. Finally, the man seated directly in front of us could stand it no longer. He stood up, turned around, and exclaimed "Listen, lady, so Sid Luckman's a Jew!", then adding "Can he help it if he's the best player out there?"

✳✳✳

The aphasic patient who perseverates on the same few words will often, though misunderstood, encounter a realistic response from their listeners, who react literally to what is continually said. In this case, the "damn shoes" had no literal meaning, so the listener took it upon himself to assume Mary Lou was berating the ethnicity of a rival team's star player.

APHASIA TALE 3

AWAY

SIMILAR to Mary Lou who could only say "damn shoes," Otto with severe aphasia could only say "away, away, away." He would repeat the word with various meaningful inflections. If he were happy, it could be heard in the sound of his voice. If he was angry, his mood showed itself with an angry "away." He presented a great challenge to the professional staff, to his family and friends, all of whom often took his "away" literally. The early management of Otto's recovery from aphasia was thwarted by the misinterpretation by others that Otto was never happy wherever he happened to be.

***

As a retired insurance man, Otto was used to making decisions and influencing others to follow his recommendations. So when the paramedics came to his home in the early morning hours following his stroke, his remark, "away, away" was believable due to the urgent necessity to leave his lakefront home for the hospital. Once admitted to his hospital room, his wife arrived, only to be greeted with "away." She likely either answered him with some description of his illness and the need for a probable long hospital stay, or interpreted his "away" as a dismissal uttered bluntly, in which case she may have responded accordingly.

During Otto's days in the hospital, ward personnel and occasional visitors were always greeted with "away, away, away." Most everyone countered with something like "Don't worry, you'll be going home soon." At his discharge planning conference his wife alleged "If you'd just listen to the man, you could tell that he won't be happy until he goes home." Otto's rehabilitation was consequently planned for outpatient physical therapy aimed at working on his paralyzed right arm and leg, and speech-language pathology services to focus on his aphasia.

On the day of his hospital discharge, his wife drove their car to the front door of the hospital. He was in a wheelchair pushed by a nurse with Otto happily repeating. "away!" As he got in the car, his "aways" became louder and even sounded happier. As soon as they arrived home, his wife wheeled him out to the front veranda overlooking the lake. Otto looked out, gesturing with a sweeping motion of his normal left arm, and in a crying voice said "away, away." According to his wife, who witnessed the scene, Otto's daughter answered him with a cry, "But, Daddy you're home now, there's no other place to go."

✳✳✳

As Otto experienced some recovery from aphasia, he eventually reduced his "away" repetitions. His leg function improved a bit, allowing him to ambulate easily with a cane. His right arm and hand remained partially paralyzed, but he was successfully trained to write with his normal left hand. He received six months of successful speech-language therapy. Otto and his wife joined a university aphasia support group, where they enjoyed sharing with others the many unfortunate reactions they experienced when all he could say was "away." Today, Otto enjoys fully functional, relatively normal speech.

APHASIA TALE 4

WATER, WATER, WATER

SIMILAR to the woman who could only say "damn shoes" and Otto with his one-word "away," Helen could only say "water." Helen, an Associate Dean in a College of Nursing, loves to tell students of the frustrating time she had following a stroke that sent her to the hospital, only able to say one word, "water." She enjoys laughing about it now, but at the time of her hospital stay, it brought her nothing but misery.

***

Helen was the best known patient on the rehabilitation ward at University Hospital, because prior to her stroke, she was the Associate Dean of the College of Nursing. Many of the ward nurses and aides knew her from previous courses they had taken with her. Helen was a close friend to many. There was nothing any shift of nurses wouldn't do for Helen. Her every wish was their command.

Helen's motor aphasia left her with very good comprehension of what was said, but with a total inability to speak any word other than "water." "Water" was her response each time anyone greeted her, and through appropriate inflection, her moods were conveyed.

When each new shift of nurses came on duty and visited patients, priority was given to Helen. She would greet them with a friendly, "water, water, water." The nursing staff, along with others who came to visit her, would assume she was thirsty, refill her water pitcher, and offer her a glass. Rather than drinking the water, Helen would respond with a perturbed "water!"

* * *

When Helen had recovered to a point where she could comfortably recount her time spent in hospitalization, she recalled one night on the ward:

Desperate for the nurse to bring her a much needed bedpan, Helen's compromised communicative abilities got her no relief for her distended bladder. "Water, water" she would say and in came the nurse with the 'cause' of her predicament, another pitcher of water.

CIRCLING OVER DALLAS

CAPTAIN D. had been a commercial airline pilot from the time he was 28 years old, until he was forced to retire at age 60. About five years after leaving the airline, Captain D. had a stroke that left him with a profound fluent aphasia. When first seen in our aphasia clinic, the Captain appeared as a handsome older man, free of any motor weakness of arm or leg, but he spoke with a rather profound jargon. Typical of this kind of jargon aphasia patient, he was unaware of his own speech errors. Consequently, he spoke freely with normal English rhythm, but his language contained many neologisms (made up words) spoken in a twisted word order. There were, however, enough occasional real words that a listener could grossly understand what he was talking about. Captain D. had difficulty following spoken commands, and his reading ability was dramatically reduced from what had obviously been superior in his work as an airline pilot. The brief interview that follows was recorded about five months after the onset of his stroke.

* * *

Boone: They tell me, Captain, that you were an airline pilot.

Captain D: Well, here's a granching thought that I flew the big one, starting with DC 4s and throttling the props cathings for a living. Stayed with the pilot casing all the way through the DC 10, which by the way, was the finest coredevil that evet toomover the country and promorthing the world.

Boone: You were a captain flying DC 10s? I've enjoyed flying as a passenger in them.

Captain D: Yes, well the proudest outfit of the Douglas parade was the ten

that could go anywhere, but she never made a noise about it. I had
one toubler with a tenner when she was about out of fuel circling over
Dallas. We had chagened all the trando from New York Kennedy and
radio shooting and by the time we go to Dallas, she was weydown with
one hell of a staroom over never again. We had no idea that the scarshun
tenfa was even torping to anyone. We couldn't get the bid won when we
tried fuging to circling and she selaid you cannot get her down, so we
circled over Dallas till our three hungry acalameters were going to run
out of kerosenedine.

Boone: Well, did you ever get to land there?

Captain D: Hell, they had a diversfication that would put pimples on your
belly button for the asking for some damn permission to set the tenner
down on their gladden fallen runway. So I took her and everbody in het
up to Austin.

✱✱✱

The Captain liked to talk about particular flying events from his career. If he
understood the gist of one's question, he would often ramble on, looking closely
at his listeners' faces to see if they were still interested in what he was saying.
He received months of individual speech-language therapy with heavy emphasis
on auditory feedback. In therapy, we forced him to track closely what was said
to him, and encouraged close self monitoring of what he was saying. I last saw
the Captain several years ago, and he was speaking with near normal speech,
enjoying fishing in his retirement.

APHASIA TALE 6

YOUR PENCHANT FOR APPLES?

THE first encounter with a new patient, particularly one with aphasia, is most important for developing a good working relationship between the patient and clinician. Adult patients with aphasia have had a life-time of using normal language until the precipitating event, such as an accident or stroke. It is important, when they may show difficulty speaking, to still approach them with the assumption that they can speak, and that they understand all that is said to them. I learned over time to approach new aphasic patients, who had been referred to me by their doctors, with this kind of approach: "Good morning. I am Doctor Boone. I work here in the hospital with patients who may be having trouble talking. I wanted to check with you. Are you having any trouble speaking or understanding what is said to you?" A patient who has no problem will not be offended by such a question. The patient with aphasia will demonstrate his problem when attempting to answer the question.

In my early days as a graduate assistant seeing patients with aphasia for the first time in hospitals, I remember a few awkward situations like this 'apples' story. I had been requested to see a see a sixty-four year old business executive in his private room for his problems with aphasia. When making our first visit for such an evaluation, we usually brought along a small testing kit that included pictures, a few objects, a paper and pencil. When I visited this man, the first thing I wanted to find out was his ability to repeat words after me, which would give some direction as to what kind of aphasia he had, as well as give me some idea of what to test first.

As I entered his room carrying my testing kit, he was sitting up in bed looking as if he was reading the morning paper. Many patients with aphasia may look as if they are reading, but may not understand the words they see. In any case, I interrupted him and said, "Good Morning, I'm Mister Boone. Your doctor wanted me to see you about your speech. I understand you've been having some trouble talking since your stroke."

He put his paper down, took off his reading glasses and gave me a long look. "I had a few days there where it was hard to talk." He looked at me again for a long time before asking, "What is it you want to know?"

"Well, it looks like your words are coming out pretty well." Attempting to take control of the situation, I said, "Let's just see how you can say things after me." I made no attempt to get to know him as a person. As he kept staring intently at me, I became a bit flustered and quickly added, "You say after me what I say. Are you ready?" Hardly waiting for his reply, I gave him in a loud voice the first word to repeat, "Apple."

The man threw his newspaper down on the bed and asked, "What's going on here?"

Flustered by his obvious annoyance but hanging in with the examination, I continued, "Can you say 'apple'? Let me hear you say, 'apple'."

"What the hell is this penchant you have for apples?" He stared me down, waiting for my response.

I replied not thinking, "I don't have anything for apples, sir, I just wanted to find out if you could say it."

"Well, son, there are all kinds of apples: there are Winesap and Delicious and Granny Smith. What is going on in your mind about apples?"

My examination attempt was a failure and we just talked for a few moments. He dominated me as the gray-haired executive not tolerating well the intrusion into his room by the young male student therapist.

***

The important lesson I learned from my apple encounter with the executive (who probably had experienced a spontaneous recovery from aphasia before I saw him) is always to preface your speech examinations by getting to know the patient as a person rather than as someone with a clinical condition. And another thing that I learned from this encounter that has been widely used by me throughout my teaching years: always have patience with young people who are learning a clinical craft and demonstrate tolerance for their mistakes.

APHASIA TALE 7

Honolulu Annie

MOST speech-language therapy for adults who have acquired aphasia is provided on an individual basis between the patient and the pathologist (SLP). The clinician may incorporate within the therapy session a family member, a speech aide, or a student SLP. Therapy emphasis is given to encouraging the patient to communicate, using words, gestures, pictures, objects, or anything that will "get the message across." Increasing communication effectiveness is the therapy goal even without saying words per se. My own particular therapy bias was heavy on listening and talking with little emphasis given to reading and writing tasks,

From my early days at the Long Beach VA Hospital, I always supplemented individual therapy with group therapy. We would typically limit the size of the group to five to seven aphasia patients, with the group coordinated by myself and an assistant (usually a graduate student.) We kept as little structure to our groups as possible, encouraging spontaneous communication, often punctuated with patient laughter. The group therapy leader had to be sure that all patients communicated at their top ability level within the session. This talking tale, Honolulu Annie, describes briefly the communication thrusts of six aphasia group patients reacting to Annie and her fun hula dance while sitting in a wheelchair.

***

We had six adult folks in the group that day: Annie, age 71, a retired Hawaiian show woman; Bill, 75, a pilot friend of Clark Gable who had lived in Tucson; Joe, 52, a mathematics college professor who could say nothing but "pretty good;" Keith, 77, a big band piano player who played with Harry James; Priscilla, 63, who had managed a coffee shop; and Marie, 81, a house-wife who lived for her home flower garden. This excerpt of a fun group session was video recorded on the day Annie had promised to come to the group wearing her Hawaiian grass skirt complete with floral lei.

Boone: "Look at Annie sitting there like Hilo Hattie." Boone points to Annie wearing her grass skirt and sitting in her wheelchair.

Bill: "God damn and looks like Hilo Hattie to me."

Joe: "Pretty good, pretty good" (smiling big and gesturing with his normal left arm and hand.)

Boone: "Hilo Hattie? How many remember her?" Several patients did remember the performer, Hilo Hattie.

Marie: As she begins to tell Annie, "Well, you should be, as I remember, your flowers are gorgeous and," two student clinicians wheel in the spinet piano.

Many of us were all talking at once but Keith says in a louder voice, "Music, music. I hear a song coming on." He gets out of his chair and walks with a slight limp to the piano. He strums the piano keys and drums out what sounds like the Hawaiian War Chant, with a fast pulsating beat. Joe and Bill mix their "God damns, its going to be" and "pretty good" with a lot of laughter. Priscilla looks a bit confused as to what is going on, but begins tapping her toes to Keith's piano rhythms.

Boone: "Priscilla, what can we have to drink at a Hawaiian party?" She has difficulty answering. Priscilla has right hemiplegia but like Annie lifts her arms high and makes circular movements with her fingers.

Annie: "Oh, boy," she begins singing "lawanna, lawanna, kanna" and picks up the beat with Keith repeating the same Hawaiian sounding words. The whole group spontaneously reacts to Keith's playing and Annie's singing with other group members singing "Pretty good," "I don't know," "God damn, it's Hilo Hattie," "Oh, darn I love this so."

Marie: "Annie, can you dance with your singing?"

Boone encourages the group to all look at Annie as she begins the best Hula dance in a wheelchair that anyone could do. She would thrust out her left leg in a seductive circle, try to sway her hips to the piano music, and go through all the hand motions needed with her good left hand.

Annie: Singing and doing the hula the best she could, she sang "lawanna, lawanna, kanna…"

✳✳✳

A critical observer might view this session and ask, "That is group therapy?" I would have to answer that it was a marvelous session, allowing each participant to participate in a spontaneous musical event. We had the piano music, the wheelchair song and dance, and the people clapping and laughing in response to Annie's hula. That morning, the six of them were people, not patients.

II

TALES OF DEMENTIA

While patients with aphasia have normal time and place orientation, patients with dementia experience difficulties knowing the when and where of the present and the past. The normal older population demonstrates good receptive and expressive language, demonstrating on occasion a slight immediate memory recall problem with excellent long-term memory. In normal aging, the older person often complains of this occasional inability to remember a particular word or the name or place of a person. The dementia patient demonstrates severe retrieval problems in naming recall and in the recall of immediate and past events. The dementia patient often shows remarkably good speech and articulation skills with normal language syntax (word order), but lacks cognitive and semantic relevance. What they say may sound like normal speech and language, but the content makes little sense.

The majority of dementia patients have dementia of the Alzheimer's type. It seems to come on gradually in a linear fashion. Unlike the unilateral involvement of the brain seen in aphasia (usually left hemisphere), Alzheimer's disease involves brain structures symmetrically (both left and right brain hemispheres.) The next most prevalent adult dementia is multi-infarct dementia, caused by the patient experiencing a series of minor strokes, with behavioral deficits developing in more of a "stair-step fashion." In multi-infarct dementia, the patient will experience more abrupt behavioral changes than in the Alzheimer patient.

Occasionally, we see aphasia patients who also show developing problems of dementia. The first dementia tale, **That Would Be, Daniel R. Boone, Ph.D.**, represents such a case. Cass, 76 years old, had been in our aphasia support group for several years at the University of Arizona before showing some of the confusions of Alzheimer's disease. The second tale, **Remember the Old Hiawatha**, was told by an ex-high school teacher, age 55, with Alzheimer's and with normal sounding speech and normal grammar and syntax. He spoke in a detached manner, sounding like a monologue, lacking any voice inflection or concern for listener reaction. A university professor, his wife, and his students deal with early Alzheimer's disease in **Where Was My Mind Today? The Clothespin** was told by a 78 year-old woman with moderately severe Alzheimer's disease. Although she showed normal speech articulation and language syntax, what she said lacked any cognitive reality. A speech-language pathologist hoped to orient a 74 year-old woman with Alzheimer's by working with old family photographs as told in the final dementia tale, **The Family Picture**. The reaction he received will never be forgotten.

THAT WOULD BE, DANIEL R. BOONE, PH.D.

IT is well recognized in medicine that a patient may have two or more diseases at the same time, related or unrelated. Cass, age 76, had two independent diseases: aphasia from a stroke followed by dementia. Some years prior to our first meeting, Cass had had a stroke that left her with severe semantic aphasia. She struggled to find proper words, but physically had normal arm and leg motor functions. As she fought to find her words, she developed a perseverative phrase, "That would be," which prefaced almost everything she attempted to say. More recently, she developed a second disease, Alzheimer's, and experienced the early symptoms of confusion specific to time and place. We do not often see patients with aphasia who then develop dementia. Her tale is an interesting one.

***

At 72, Cass had a stroke that caused aphasia from which she made almost no speech recovery in the four ensuing years. She said "that would be" as her primary spoken response in almost any situation. However, after joining our aphasia support group at the University of Arizona and working directly with me, she modified her "that would be" by adding my complete name and degree to the utterance. Whenever she talked, she would smile and say, "That would be, Daniel R. Boone, Ph.D."

This response proved to be a continuous problem for me. After her dementia took over, Cass used to leave her apartment and walk to the University campus, quickly becoming lost among the 35,000 students and myriad of offices and buildings. As Cass wandered lost on campus, people would react to her "That would be, Daniel R. Boone, Ph. D.?" by looking promptly for this Ph.D. in the University directory. Subsequently, they would either walk her to my office or call me. More often than not, this necessitated me or an associate to drive her home.

As her dementia worsened, we were forced to drop her from the aphasia support group. However, this did not end my contact with Cass; in fact, our visits increased. She soon began walking within a few miles from her apartment asking people she met on the street, "That would be, Daniel R. Boone, Ph.D.?" with the tone of a question sounding in her voice. At almost any time of the day or night, I would receive a phone call from an unknown person saying that a nice woman was lost and was looking for a "Doctor Boone." Once it became apparent to her relatives and neighbors that she was no longer able to live unattended (by accident and confusion, she had started two stove fires in her apartment,) she was moved into a nursing care facility.

∗∗∗

Fortunately for me, in time my name dropped out of Cass's perseverative speech pattern. If she did say it, personnel realized that my name was about all she could say and did not take her words as a literal request for my presence.

DEMENTIA TALE 2

REMEMBER THE OLD HIAWATHA?

IT is not unusual among dementia patients to find people who speak with great clarity about events from their remote past, but are unable to recall anything about what just happened. Long term memory may be excellent while short term memory may be wholly lacking. Tom was such a patient. A former high school teacher, at age fifty-five he was diagnosed as having Alzheimer's disease. The onset of Alzheimer's disease often begins with patients considerably older than Tom.

***

In order to establish rapport with Tom and to provide some indication of his orientation to time and place I asked him, "Do you still live in Tucson?" His reply prompted this detailed narrative of an incident he had experienced as a boy:

"I came here from Illinois. I was raised in Deerfield, a good drive north of Chicago. The Willmans lived across the road and you had to cross through their apple orchard, if you remember, to reach the railway tracks and then walk a half a mile after that. I used to go through there, usually picking an apple, even though old lady Willman didn't like it, about once a week on my way to see the Hiawatha. You may remember the old Hiawatha? She used to come roaring through Deerfield out of Chicago on her way to Minneapolis-St. Paul. She was the flagship of the old Milwaukee Line. She was painted orange with a red stripe and, boy, could she travel. Used to come through there about sixty miles an hour. I can remember my mama telling me, 'Don't get too near the tracks, Tommy, it's going over a mile a minute and it might suck you in as it's going by.' But I knew that train would never hurt me. I remember her like it was yesterday, all golden, and one of the first streamliners they ever made. You could wave to the people in her cars and every now and then, one of them would wave back. There was always somebody in the last car who'd wave at you, almost as if the train was telling you 'hello.' One time no one waved and I remember the Hiawatha tooting back at me as she went down the track to Waukegan. It was like she was apologizing for the folks in her that couldn't take the time to wave back at me. They don't make trains like the Hiawatha anymore. You had to tramp through the Willman's apples to get to the tracks, but the Hiawatha would always pay you back with a nice hello when you got there. The Hiawatha, do you remember her?"

✳✳✳

In later observation of Tom, I found that he often repeated the Hiawatha story to anyone who seemed to want to listen to him. He spoke with clear speech but his voice appeared a bit higher in pitch than normal without any kind of word inflection. He seemed unaware of his listener response, giving most of the time a non-interactive monologue. About a half hour after our first meeting, I talked with him again. He appeared to have no recognition of me as someone who had just been with him. He greeted me with, "Do you remember the old Hiawatha?"

WHERE WAS MY MIND TODAY?

THE typical older voice patient may have several competing medical, physical, or mental problems that may interfere with what we try to accomplish in voice therapy. Dr. S., a 64-year old Professor in the Department of Geosciences was such an example. In the beginning of his voice problem, he had experienced some throat discomfort and noticeable voice hoarseness after lecturing for several hours to successive classes. On laryngeal examination, he was found to have "a normal larynx", and the subsequent voice evaluation identified a moderate problem of vocal hyperfunction. He was working too hard to speak. Early in voice therapy we had good luck producing greater relaxation, better breath support, and softening his way of speaking. After two weeks of twice weekly voice therapy sessions, he missed two successive appointments. When asked about the absences, he could only say that he had forgotten about the appointments.

After missing three out of four more subsequent appointments, he apologized again for not writing down the appointment times and dates. In the fifth week, he came to the clinic with his wife, Cora, who told us confidentially that her husband had shown in recent months a series of forgotten events. One time she related that Dr. S. had presented the wrong lecture to a large class of undergraduates in an introductory geology class. What he had started to present with detailed slides was an advanced lecture for a graduate seminar. He was embarrassed by his mistake as the students left the classroom early. Dr. S. went back to his office and scribbled a note to himself, "Where was my mind today." A few students had even reported the inappropriate lecture to the college dean. Cora told us that his mental confusions had become more public and far more serious than any other problem he had recently experienced, such as his hoarseness.

* * *

We had realized that his mental confusions relative to time and place had become his primary problem. Voice therapy was no longer appropriate. His wife reported that on several occasions he had become lost driving home from the University, a route he had routinely driven for over twenty years. She also described his crying frustration after he discovered he had lost his boxed collection of rare rock samples that he had collected over a life time. He wondered if he had accidentally "thrown it away." His biggest upset was the day he mistakenly deleted from his computer many pages of manuscript he had been working on for many months.

Dr. S. continued to try to keep his geology teaching load. In his office, he kept several calendars with explanatory notes telling him where to go, at what time to be there, and what to do after he got there. He appeared normal in both his speech and use of language. His voice seemed to no longer be a problem. The departmental secretary did what he could to minimize the professor's confusions. While most students seemed to accept his confusions and recognized his superior professional knowledge base, a few had fun exaggerating a situation and laughing at his mistakes. His professor colleagues more and more recognized his mental changes and did what they could do in the beginning to keep him oriented to some of his teaching tasks. As his confusions continued to increase, however, he was finally diagnosed as having beginning stages of Alzheimer's disease. Before the end of the semester, he was forced to take a permanent early retirement.

* * *

During the early stages of Alzheimer's disease, casual speaking ability often appears normal, particularly specific to word choice and grammar. Lapses of content adequacy may occur, but the good speaking ability can often mask the patient's occasional mental shortcomings. For individuals in authority and verbal positions (such as professors, lawyers, managers), Alzheimer patients may be able to hide in the beginning some of their mental confusions. These early confusions seem inconsistent with the patient's life time history of punctuality and appropriateness. In the beginning, a patient like Dr. S. will attempt to keep his orientation by calendar self-notes. When such patients miss appointments or become confused as to where they should be, the patient and family will make excuses, which in the beginning are accepted by others.

After the early stages of the disease, when the patient becomes less aware of the world around him, the suffering of Alzheimer's disease transfers from the patient to the spouse and family. Over the last five years we have kept close contact with the Professor's wife, Cora, and through talking with her have watched the progression of his dementia. In the early stages of the disease, she did what she could do to "cover" for her husband's confusions. For the first two years after his diagnosis of Alzheimer's, Cora and other family members did everything possible to keep him within their home. The need for increasing nursing care and his increasing demands for attention (often punctuated by useless arguments) forced Cora to require outside help. Finally, her case-worker at a regional center on aging recommended that he be placed in a nursing care facility with other dementia patients. Such a place was found not too far from the family home.

Cora continued to make twice-weekly visits to see him, despite her gradual realization that he no longer recognized her. It always saddened me when I remember what she said at our last visit together, "When you folks worked on his voice, he made such an improvement. When he became so confused, I had hoped there would also be possible some successful treatment. But with this Alzheimer's thing, the one you knew and loved just slowly disappears on you."

I wish we could have done more. Dr. S. recently died from an infection, unrelated to his Alzheimer's disease.

DEMENTIA TALE 4

THE CLOTHESPIN

FOR many years, we were studying the verbal abilities of patients with dementia at the University of Arizona. In general, we found that patients with dementia could speak surprisingly well. While the content of what they said may not have had much meaning, the way they said it (sounds of speech, grammar, vocabulary) often sounded like that of a person with normal functioning intelligence. Mary, age 81, with moderately severe Alzheimer's disease well illustrated the contrast in demonstrating normal grammar and vocabulary, but not making much sense to her listeners.

***

As part of our battery of tests for measuring speech and language in dementia patients, we included a task of naming objects followed by a request to tell us what the objects were used for. The patient was shown five objects, one at a time, and asked to name each one and tell us something about it. Mary was presented a clothespin and I asked her, "What is this?"

Holding the clothespin in her right hand, she turned it over several times so that she could examine it closely, and then said, "This, of course, is just a wood thickness, and then they have the wood itself. And we could pinch it which years ago would have been a horrible looking thing, wouldn't it? And here we have it where the wood would be."

Interrupting her, I asked again, "What is it?"

"Well, some years ago and for so many times you used it for a clothespin. This is what started it and to have it. It might get here and here and here, but it never got in this way. Likewise, they thought that they would, but because it became larger and was part of the picture, people liked it. It took over. That's all it was. Then we had something else with it."

Attempting to move on to naming the next object, I took the clothespin back and said, "So, it's a clothespin, right?"

She smiled and added, "The clothespin had its way and we'd never got too far without it. Whenever we needed it, it was around us. It was going to be something, if it had its way. And then stopped it all after finding it was a clothespin."

∗∗∗

This elaborate answer when asked to identify an object is a typical response of a moderately severe dementia patient on a naming task. Grammar, vocabulary, and word order are relatively normal. The extensive elaboration, however, carries little or no meaning. On our 5-item naming test, the typical dementia patient seems unable to give a one-word naming response. Although they may say the word in their elaborate reply, they seem to show almost no awareness of listener response. A wife commenting on her husband's dementia and difficulty in naming things stated, "He always seems to be forced to keep raving about the object, talking on and on about it, completely unaware that he is making no sense to me." Specific naming in dementia is often a difficult task.

THE FAMILY PICTURE

PEARL, 74 years old, had a twenty year history of vascular hypertension with elevated cholesterol, for which medical treatment had been basically ineffective. In the 1950s and 1960s, elevated cholesterol was principally treated through dietary reduction of fats. Subsequently, in her early seventies she began to experience several small strokes. This was followed by occasional episodes of time and place confusion. In the beginning of her confusions, she was aware of her problem but unable to correct it on her own. She also began to show some confusion while dressing, such as trying to put her left foot in her right shoe. Her loving husband reported that she became increasingly emotionally labile when she found herself confused, often lashing out at those around her. On medical examination she was found to have "multi-infarct dementia," deteriorating brain function resulting from a "continuous series of small vascular strokes."

In the beginning, her physical appearance stayed the same, often looking like the lady who could preside over the tea. As her dementia worsened, her husband reported that if he left her alone in their house, she might unmake the beds, take down the drapes, and get out the luggage. She would then say with normal speech, "I think we'd better get going." Her behaviors within her home and later in the home of her daughter continued to worsen, such as continuing to empty kitchen and bedroom drawers, and packing her own clothing into the drawers she had emptied. The family eventually realized that Pearl had to be cared for outside the home in a nursing care facility.

***

Pearl's two adult children and her husband all took an active role in seeing that her care was good in the understaffed nursing facility. As the dementia increased, her behaviors became worse. She was observed several times by visiting members of her family to be walking naked down the halls, dropping into the rooms of other dementia patients to give afternoon greetings. Her need to undress herself and pile her clothes on her bed required continued monitoring by nursing staff. After six months in the nursing home, she began to dig and scratch out the grout between the tiles in her bathroom, placing the grout in her mouth, chewing and swallowing it. She was even observed scratching out tile grout in other patients' bathrooms.

Within two years of the onset of her dementia, she could no longer recognize family members when they came to visit her. Her son, a doctoral level speech-language pathologist (SLP), attempted to provide her with some mental focus by reviewing with her old pictures of family members. He selected a picture of his four children and placed it in front of both of them on a table. He kept his mother's attention by speaking in a louder voice, pointing to each child by name. Pearl seemed to be looking as she talked a bit in a normal voice about "nothing." She gave no evidence of picture recognition.

Finally, as a closing gesture, Pearl's son said, "OK, mom, let me get you a glass of water." He got up from the table and went to the sink in the room and filled a paper cup with water. When he returned, the family picture was no longer on the table. He could see in Pearl's open mouth that she was chewing it and had already swallowed two-thirds of it. The son looked in disbelief as his mother had eaten their family picture.

✳✳✳

Fortunately for Pearl and her family, the dementia that had taken over her person had a quick ending. About four years after onset, her grout eating behavior caused a massive internal hemorrhage, leading to her sudden death. The SLP son was always fascinated by the incongruity between his mother's severe cognitive decline and her continuing abilities to speak with articulation clarity and normal grammar and syntax. This personal experience with his mother's dementia, together with his professional career investigating aphasia and providing language service for people with aphasia, led to years of published dementia and language studies at the University of Arizona. I am this SLP. Pearl was my mother.

III

TALES OF NEUROGENIC DISORDERS

We have looked at aphasia and dementia with a mixture of laughter and tears. We now look at neurological disorders and their particular impact on patients and the people around them. A particular disease or trauma to the brain or spinal column is classified as a **neurological** disorder. The term **neurogenic** applies to the cause of a clinical behavior that has its origins from a particular neurological disorder.

One of the speech-language pathologists' (SLP) tasks with neurogenic communication patients is to search for residual abilities that have not been altered by the faulty neurological system. Also, there is usually a functional overlay to various sensory or motor disabilities experienced by the neurologically impaired person. That is, patients with the same disorder will function or respond in different ways from one another, depending on such variables as personality, motivation, family reactions, living situations, and/or availability of professional services. While habilitation of neurogenic communication disorders cannot usually alter the cause or maintenance of the problem, overall communication abilities can often be raised by the SLP reducing distractions, finding optimum response situations, and listening/watching closely to the needs of the person.

Although we'll keep our descriptions of various neurogenic disorders as free of medical jargon as possible, we will define a few conditions that affect communication. Unlike the speech and language variations heard in aphasia, **dysarthria** is a motor speech problem. The dysarthric patient's speech is compromised in different ways: slurred articulation, altered speaking rate, and/or voice quality and resonance distortions. Dysarthria is a frequent consequence of such disorders as stroke, cerebral palsy, brain-injury, Parkinson's disease, multiple sclerosis, amyotrophic lateral sclerosis, and many other lesser known degenerative diseases of the nervous system. Dysarthria may be caused in part by **paresis** (muscle weakness) or **paralysis** (absent or spastic muscle action.) Lack of central muscle coordination or respiratory difficulties are often contributing factors to the motor speech problem.

Apraxia is the inability to perform a purposeful motor act on command, but able to perform the same motor task spontaneously (when not asked to do so.) Oral apraxia, a motor disorder involving primarily lips, jaw movement, and tongue can exist isolated by itself or found in combination with expressive aphasia or with some dysarthrias. For example, the patient with oral apraxia may be unable on request to blow on an unlit match; however, when the match is lit, the patient can blow out the burning match immediately. The marked distinction between the inability to perform an intentional motor act (blowing on the unlit match) contrasted with normal function for the same act done spontaneously (blowing on the flame) is always an amazing clinical phenomenon to observe. **Gait apraxia** is equally amazing. Gait apraxia is often seen in association with Parkinson's disease where the patient will have difficulty walking through an open door but have no difficulty walking across a room. In some neuropathological conditions, the patient may have apraxia for raising his arm on request, but have no difficulty raising it when a ball is thrown for him to catch. We will read later of a patient who had no trouble sitting automatically in a chair, but when asked to "Sit down," he demonstrated an apraxia for sitting (he could not initiate the series of movements required to sit when directed to do so.)

In this neurogenic section of **Damn Shoes and Other Talking Tales**, we look at some real life situations experienced by six neurogenic patients and the reactions of the people around them. I have used the first tale,

The Examination, in training medical and SLP students throughout my career. In the middle 1960s, I was the state consultant for cerebral palsy while teaching at the University of Kansas. This young man with cerebral palsy taught me and the students by my side not to let a patient's diagnostic label mask our ability to hear how and what the patient has to say.

The second tale, **See You Tomorrow, Bonnie**, describes the interaction between a teen aged female with cerebral palsy and her SLP, perhaps providing insight as to the danger of **SLP**s getting too close psychologically to their patients. **Come to Bed, Frank** is the story of a fireman who acquired an apraxia for sitting. As the patient, Frank, recovered totally from apraxia symptoms (caused by a massive smoke-inhalation induced encephalopathy), he looked back with humor at his temporary inability to sit on command when asked to do so by another person.

The physical ravages experienced by many people who suffer from degenerative neurological diseases are often overwhelming. One such person, a 52 year-old former tennis professional with amyotrophic lateral sclerosis, comments on his growing physical problems in **I Am a Prisoner**. We never know what to expect in the responses of the young traumatically brain-injured patient who we meet in **Dr. Lincoln**. Gait apraxia, an inability to initiate walking steps, is described in **Here Comes the Elevator** by a woman with Parkinson's. After receiving an effective medication (dopamine) regimen, she was able to reduce her gait apraxia and eventually was able to laugh at her memories of when she was unable to walk into an elevator.

NEUROGENIC TALE 1

THE EXAMINATION

THE speech-language pathologist learns early in clinical work not to prejudge patient performance by the label the patient is carrying. I learned this best while examining patients, ages one to twenty, with cerebral palsy at the University of Kansas Medical Center. I functioned as the state consultant for cerebral palsy, testing patients once a year who were brought in from around the state of Kansas. On every other Friday morning I evaluated these young patients, assisted by a few speech pathology graduate students. Each patient was tested for hearing, self-feeding skills, oral mechanism function, speech articulation competence, and expressive conversational language. I am sure that none of the students, nor I, will ever forget Ed, age 20, diagnosed as having "severe athetoid cerebral palsy."

***

As part of an orthopedic cerebral palsy clinic, we set up an evaluation booth that included an audiometer, a tape recorder, and our speech-language testing materials. Prior to each patient's arrival, the students and I selected the materials and tests we wanted to administer consistent with patient diagnosis. Athetoid patients like Ed generally displayed flailing arm movements that interfered with fine oral movements, often making clear speech impossible to produce. We planned to look closely at how Ed was able to coordinate his breath with his mouth movements for speech; this would include assessing his jaw control, tongue dexterity, and facial-lip movements. If we could understand his speech, we were going to administer an articulation test that would differentiate the sounds he could say from those he could not produce correctly. Also, athetoid cerebral palsy patients often demonstrate trouble understanding the speech of others, so we had a detailed test ready that would pinpoint his language comprehension. If he could speak several words clearly enough, we planned to assess his expressive language functions.

One of the graduate students wheeled Ed in his wheelchair into the examining room. As I looked up from my desk, I saw a young man writhing in his chair, with his head twisted to one side and his arms flailing above his head in the air. His legs were locked across one another above his ankles. Such writhing movements quickly confirmed in my mind that his "severe athetoid" diagnosis was correct. Nodding at the students to begin the examination, I moved over to the patient and introduced myself. Thinking he might be hard of hearing, I said in a louder than normal voice, "I'm Doctor Boone, good morning."

Ed quickly looked up at me and said with normal speech, "Tell me Doctor, what does this communication examination entail?"

Startled by his clear, intelligent question, I mumbled back, "Well, in your case, I don't think it will entail much."

✳✳✳

His appearance and his diagnostic label had not told us that he was a junior at the University of Kansas. All we tested was his hearing that day, as he demonstrated better speech and language than most of his examiners.

SEE YOU TOMORROW, BONNIE

ARLY in my doctoral training program in the early 1950s, I lived on the grounds and worked at Highland View Hospital in Cleveland. Half of the patient population was an elderly custodial population; the remaining half of the patient population (about 175 people) consisted of neurogenic patients participating in an active rehabilitation program. Three speech-language pathologists (SLPs) provided the speech-language services (evaluation and therapy) that were needed. While the majority of rehabilitation patients were post-stroke, we had a surprising number of multiple sclerosis (MS) patients, Parkinson's disease (PD), amyotrophic lateral sclerosis (ALS), and some with traumatic head or spinal cord injuries.

We also had a special population of 15 cerebral palsy (CP) patients, aging from 12 to 35 years, all of whom received intensive medical and rehabilitation care. The CP patients were part of a long-term study to see if intensive rehabilitation (physical and occupational therapy, vocational training, and speech pathology services) would help in the future for each individual to function more independently. Of some interest to the curious reader, the eight CP patients who with rehabilitation therapies improved the most, reaching some degree of functional independence, were those who demonstrated less motor involvement in the beginning of their rehab program. Several of the severe patients, often with combined spasticity/athetoid muscle problems, showed almost no improvement.

This talking tale is about the fifteenth patient in the long-term study. Her name was Bonnie. She was 14 yrs old with moderately severe athetoid cerebral palsy. Besides her flailing arms and legs, she had developed a severe spinal scoliosis (her thoracic spine curved severely to the right.) Consequently, as she sat in her wheelchair, her upper body, neck, and head leaned moderately to her right.

***

Bonnie worked with me in individual speech therapy sessions for three half-hours a week. We had a dual therapy focus, working on improving chewing/swallowing (improving vertical posturing and developing better mouth closure) and improving speech intelligibility (matching auditory modeling with her own productions.) She also participated twice weekly with five or six other patients in a CP support group (a favorite task was trying to resist reacting with startle responses to sudden auditory and visual stimuli.) There was also time for spontaneous conversation, laughter, and occasional tears.

Bonnie had a teenage "crush" on this clinician, particularly because her favorite singer was Pat Boone. My name was not only "Boone", but I had met and talked with Pat Boone on a plane trip to Chicago. As a young, newly married man, Bonnie took extra interest in meeting my wife (a PT in our program) and our baby girl. My attempts to change her SLP from me to a female colleague on our staff, proved to be very upsetting to Bonnie. So I stayed with her.

The assistant medical physiatrist on our CP project became increasingly concerned about the growing severity of Bonnie's spinal scoliosis. At one of our staff conferences, it was decided that Bonnie required orthopedic surgical intervention to correct her spinal deformity. Some concern was raised about her athetoid flailing movements presenting a real obstacle to the healing process after surgery. To prevent such movements of her body, it was decided Bonnie would have to wear post-surgically a body cast for six to eight weeks to stabilize her torso. Some staff raised concern that she might not be able to tolerate wearing such a rigid post-operative cast, since for a lifetime she had continuous flailing movements of her arms and legs, which seemed to accentuate the bending of her torso. The orthopedic surgeon said flatly that he would not be able to correct the curve in her spine unless she wore the body cast for at least six weeks after the surgery.

Therefore, a trial body cast was placed around her six weeks before the scheduled surgery. If she could not tolerate it, the cast would be removed and the planned surgery would be cancelled. Bonnie tolerated the cast well for six weeks. Inhibiting her uncontrolled movements had actually improved our work with her in both feeding and speaking. We talked freely about the coming operation day when the cast would be removed, the surgery completed, with a new body cast then put in place. When that final cast was removed, she would then be able to sit and even walk in an upright position, as she said, "like everyone else."

I joined much of the staff in explaining to Bonnie and her family how much better she would be able to do things after the surgery. The surgery was scheduled for a Monday morning. I remember well my visit to Bonnie in her hospital bed early Sunday evening with her single parent, her mother, sitting next to her. I remember kissing her on the forehead and Bonnie kissing me on the cheek. I remember telling her goodbye with a little assurance when I said, "See you tomorrow, Bonnie, after the operation."

Bonnie died the next morning in the operating room.

∗∗∗

Apparently, Bonnie died as a reaction to the anesthetic. Her weeks in the body cast with the enforced lack of body movement before the procedure had weakened her total system. I had become very fond of Bonnie as a person. I questioned my medical colleagues after her death about the necessity of restricting motor movements in a young patient with cerebral palsy, who had spent her short life-time with hyperactive motor activity, twisting her torso and flailing her extremities.

Her sudden death bothered me. More than a clinician working on swallowing and talking, I had become a close friend. I, also, learned a career lesson: never become too close emotionally with a patient. With any kind of negative outcome, such closeness can really take a toll on the clinician.

Come To Bed, Frank

SOME patients after brain damage have problems of apraxia. As mentioned in our introduction, apraxia is the inability to do things on purpose (like blowing on an unlit match) contrasted with normal motor movements for automatic functions (like blowing out a lit match as it is brought closer to one's mouth). In apraxia, there is a dramatic difference between normal function for automatic situations and the complete inability to perform "on purpose" or volitional movements. Some apraxia patients have problems in moving their mouths, or some cannot take a step if told to do so. Frank, age 37, was a victim of an unusual apraxia, an inability to sit down if told to do so by someone else. He could sit down normally if he were not asked to do so.

***

Frank was an athletic fireman, 37 years old, in excellent health until the day he inhaled a large amount of toxic smoke while fighting a plastic fire. The continuous exposure to these fumes resulted in an "encephalopathy" which affected parts of his brain, resulting (among other symptoms) an apraxia for sitting down.

Referred to my office for a speech evaluation in a rehabilitation hospital, I observed that Frank had some difficulty sitting down. When the office receptionist told Frank to sit down in the waiting room, he replied, "Oh, I wish you hadn't said that." He consequently remained standing until I came out and ushered him into my office. As we talked casually walking into my office, I motioned for him to sit down. Instead of sitting in the chair in front of my desk, he stood behind it, and then circled around it several times, saying "Oh, I wish you hadn't pointed to the chair." If someone told him to sit or even pointed to a sitting place, he could not sequence the correct motor movements to sit down. After bending his knees several times and hopping to the front of the chair, he was finally able to lower his body into the seat.

Once comfortably seated, Frank told me, "It's the damndest thing, Doc. Since my accident, I can't sit down if someone tells me to do it. If I walk in a room on my own and see a chair or a bed, I can sit down with no problem." He was describing the classic symptoms of apraxia, the inability to do with intention what he can do automatically.

Frank and I became good friends during his hospital stay. He volunteered to help us with a much needed service, pushing wheelchair patients from their wards to our speech clinic and back to their rooms when the speech therapy appointment was over. He had no problem in walking or in taking the patient to the clinic. At times, when accompanying a patient, he would come into the waiting room, sit down (fortunately, no one told him to), and have a cup of coffee with patients while they waited for their appointments.

After being an inpatient in our rehabilitation hospital for four weeks, I participated with other professionals in Frank's discharge planning conference. His wife also attended the conference. She told us about the problems she had with Frank's sitting when he first came home on a weekend pass. Apparently, after they both got dressed for bed, she got in bed first. As Frank approached the bed, she made the mistake of saying "Come to bed, Frank." Immediately, Frank began bending down in a tight circle trying to sit, as he cried out, "Oh, I wish you hadn't said that." According to his wife, his shifting, circling movements continued until he accidentally fell into bed.

∗∗∗

There are specific and focal movements that we all do to accomplish a motor task, such as sitting. For most of us, there is not much difference between the automatic execution of the task or deliberately doing the same movement. Frank's inability to sit on purpose (with preservation of normal automatic ability to sit) was an apraxia for sitting, a rare symptom of brain damage caused by his extensive inhalation of toxic smoke. Fortunately, within a few months after the onset of his problem, Frank made a complete recovery (no more sitting apraxia) and eventually he was able to go back to working as a fireman.

I Am a Prisoner

ABOUT a month before I evaluated Mike in our hospital department, I had talked to him casually at our mutual tennis club about a frontal lisp he felt that he was developing. Mike was 51 years old, a tennis pro, who had enjoyed a lifetime of robust health. At one time, Mike had coached me on my game of tennis, and despite my limited progress we had remained good friends. However, in the last few months, he had lost his balance on the tennis courts, and he had even fallen twice. Seeking medical help, as part of a total medical evaluation, he was referred for speech-language services regarding his increasing problem producing sibilant sounds like /s/ and /z/.

Audiological testing found Mike to have basically normal hearing with a slight high-frequency loss not atypical for his age of 51 years. Language testing was basically confined to conversation about tennis and world events, with Mike displaying normal comprehension and language. His connected speech, however, did show a slight sibilant /s/ and /z/ distortion. On a peripheral oral evaluation, he showed two abnormal tongue findings: 1) when asked to stick out his tongue and hold it out, the tongue showed fasciculation (a traveling wave across the tongue surface); and 2) he had some difficulty when asked to elevate his tongue tip up behind his upper incisors, as if he were making the /t/ sound. Particularly disturbing to me was the observation of tongue muscle fasciculation, where several fibers of a tongue muscle are twitching simultaneously, producing the wave-like movement on the surface of the protruded tongue. Our observations suggested a possible muscle problem of neurogenic origin, and he was referred for a neurological examination.

We did not see Mike again in our department for several months. He continued to work as a tennis pro, but was experiencing increased problems walking and running on the tennis courts. Further neurological observation and testing finally came up with the diagnosis of amyotrophic lateral sclerosis (ALS), often called Lou Gehrig's disease. The cause of ALS is unknown. It involves nerve tracts in the lower part of the brain and upper spinal columns and is classified as a lower motor neuron disease. There is no medical or surgical treatment available to prevent the progression of the disease. There is gradual deterioration of muscle function in both legs and arms, and involvement of tongue and throat muscles involved with speech, swallowing, and throat clearing. About four months after his ALS diagnosis, Mike experienced enough leg muscle deterioration that he was unable to work any longer teaching tennis. He spent a few hours a day in the pro shop, selling tennis goods and restringing racquets (his upper extremities remained functional.) There was some increased slurring of his speech, and he was forced to speak slower than normal, probably related in part to slower tongue movements.

We initiated speech therapy when he began to experience some difficulty feeding himself. He began to experience some choking when swallowing, particularly when drinking fluids. We worked with him on head posture, mouth closure, and attempting to increase the rate of tongue movements. Language function remained normal. We worked with him to increase speech intelligibility, making special efforts to produce tongue movements (accuracy and speed) for such sounds as /k, g, t, d/. He was a fighter for improvement and was always able to improve temporarily some function. When his speech or swallowing would worsen, Mike would come to see us intermittently over a two year period.

Although Mike's speech could still be understood, he needed our help for back throat activities related to swallowing and clearing his throat. We worked closely with nursing related to clearing out throat mucus, coughing, and the pooling of mucus-fluids in the back of his throat and under his tongue, requiring the use of a syringe when needed to suction out the fluids he couldn't clear on his own. His overall leg and body control worsened, and he was forced to use a wheelchair. I remember one of our last visits with Mike, now only 52 years old when he told us, "I am a prisoner of my own body."

✳✳✳

Mike well described his plight and the unfortunate progression of degenerative nervous system diseases, like ALS. Speech therapy, like other rehabilitation programs, can help the patient use maximally all remaining systems that have not been involved by the disease process. It cannot prevent further disease progression. Mike and his family had almost three years after the diagnosis of ALS to make as much out of life as possible. Mike remained cheerful and thoughtful of those around him, his family and church friends, tennis buddies, and the team of medical workers who provided him the care he had to have. Counseling with clergy was a great help to Mike and members of his family. Similar to other patients towards the terminal days inflicted by ALS, Mike began to breathe in (aspirate) the fluids accumulating in his throat, eventually dying from the collected fluids in his lungs. Appreciating his valiant fight for life, I will always remember him and his haunting words, "I am a prisoner of my own body."

NEUROGENIC TALE 5

DR. LINCOLN

THIS brief anecdote is included as a tale to add some levity and needed balance to this neurogenic section. Josh was a 22 year-old head trauma patient who had received four weeks of speech-language therapy. After a dramatic recovery from most of his disabilities, he was scheduled for a hospital discharge planning conference.

***

Following ten days in a coma after an automobile accident induced head injury, Josh, upon awakening, showed some motor deficits in his left arm and leg with left facial muscle weakness. He showed some cognitive deficits, inappropriate use of language, and a mild **dysphagia** (problems in swallowing). About four weeks after the accident, he had made significant improvement and was scheduled to return home to live with his mother and younger brother. Any further rehabilitation therapy could be provided him as an outpatient.

Josh was able to walk well with a cane. His mother had come to his ward and they walked together to our clinic waiting room. I came into the waiting room and announced his name. They both stood up as I extended my hand to greet them, and Josh said to his mother, "Mom, this is the man I've been working with on my speech. I want you to meet Dr. Abraham Lincoln."

Before I could correct his name selection, his mother joined in, "So glad to meet you, Dr. Lincoln."

I answered, "Well, Josh has the right idea about my having a famous American name. But it isn't Lincoln," I paused as I added; "I am Daniel Boone."

We all shared some embarrassed laughter as we went to the seminar room for our discharge planning conference.

***

For me, some questions about my ancestry or some teasing remark about my name have been common occurrences for a lifetime (I had two sons and wisely did not pass on the name "Daniel Boone.") However, this was the first time that anyone had ever mistakenly substituted my name for another historical figure. In the case of Josh, it was consistent with problems he was having in specific word recall. He knew I had the name of a famous American historical figure. He just could not remember which one.

NEUROGENIC TALE 6

HERE COMES THE ELEVATOR

ROSE, 52, had a five year history of progressive motor involvement from Parkinson's disease. Her main concern was a severe gait apraxia which at times made it impossible for her to initiate forward walking. As she attempted to walk when asked to do so, she would stand taking many short steps in place but could not step forward. Similarly, when asked to walk through a doorway, she often could not initiate the steps necessary to walk through it. Her speech had a slight dysarthria characterized by rapid articulation and a very light voice. She also had non-intention hand tremor; at rest, her hands would be tremorous but when asked to touch her nose, she could do so quickly without tremor.

This particular tale occurred in the middle 1950s when Rose was a patient active in our speech pathology program in a rehabilitation hospital.

***

While Rose was in our rehabilitation program, she received speech therapy everyday at 11:30 in the morning. Within the therapy session we focused on talking louder, even encouraging her to yell speech responses. When speaking with such deliberate intention (speaking inappropriately louder), her speech was much more normal in rhythm and clarity of articulation. Besides providing her speech therapy, it became my job every noon to walk beside her as she returned to her ward for lunch. The speech therapy offices were on the fourth floor and her ward was on the third, necessitating that we walk the length of two corridors and then negotiate the elevator. Once we got started, Rose could walk the hallway with no difficulty, shuffling ahead with small steps but in a steady gait. She would shuffle down the fourth floor hallways holding my arm until we reached the elevator. We stopped and I pushed the down-button. Rose and I then stood waiting, and we could see the numbers flash by above the door as the elevator approached our floor. About one floor ahead of the elevator's arrival, Rose began to shuffle her feet in place, moving neither forwards nor backwards. Bothered for some time by her gait apraxia, she knew that she was going to have trouble stepping into the elevator when the door quickly opened.

The elevator door would open and four or five people riding up or down would look out at us, as Rose would shuffle in place, unable to move towards the door. I took her arm, saying, "Come on, Rose, let's get on." Quickly she would answer in her rapid speech, "I would if I could, but I can't, so I can't move in." As she shuffled in place, I said to the people in the elevator, "You folks go on, we'll catch the next one."

As the elevator door closed, I pushed the down-button again. We repeated this procedure several times, each time hoping to board the elevator, but with no luck. Then I remembered that if we could set up an automatic walking situation, it would be easier for her to walk into the elevator. So I said to her, "Rose, this is how we can get on the elevator. First of all, we'll stand back further from the elevator so we'll have more room to walk. As we look up and see that the car is coming to our floor, I'll start tapping you on the arm and we'll match each tap by counting aloud together. We'll start our count just before the elevator gets here and begin walking forward towards the door. Then when the door opens, we can "just sail in as we are counting 1-2-3-4-5-6."

Our "entry" plan worked. We counted as we walked and skipped rapidly into the elevator, often startling the other passengers with our unique entrance.

Our problems, however, did not end with our boarding the car. We remembered we had the same sudden door opening problem again which would make it difficult to get out of the elevator. We soon found that we were lacking adequate walking distance to "count-walk" our way out of the elevator. We had to walk across the width of the elevator car. The door would open at the third floor, but open and close so abruptly that we couldn't easily use our counting system. I can remember astonished staff and friends looking in on us as the door opened at various floors. I would playfully yell out, "We're taking an elevator tour ride today."

Rose and I decided that as the elevator approached the third floor, we would begin our counting-walking sidewise, early enough that when the door opened, we would be scooting through. The first step was "one," the second step was "two," and so forth. It often took us a few rides down and a few rides up before we had the timing perfected so that our walk from the back of the elevator was uninterrupted in rhythm and timed exactly with the opening of the door. As the door opened, we were through it.

***

Gait apraxia is always more severe the more focal the situation, such as walking through a door the second it opens. It would have been easier for us to push Rose back to her room in a wheelchair, but part of the philosophy of the rehabilitation hospital was to encourage as much walking as possible. I am sure that many hospital staff and certainly most visitors were startled by our unorthodox style of entering or exiting the elevator.

Walking through doorways, particularly those with automatic opening doors, is particularly difficult for the rare patient with gait apraxia. Usually such an apraxia is only found in occasional patients with Parkinson's disease. Despite her attempts to diminish the gait problem in her physical therapy sessions, Rose had experienced little success. Things improved for her when a successful medication regimen (elevating combinations of dopamine, norepinephrine, and serotonin) was finally established. The last time I saw Rose, she was experiencing less gait apraxia, and she also had improved the quality of her speech and diminished some of her non-intention hand tremor. She also laughingly reminded me, "Remember when the two of us couldn't get in the elevator? And when we got in, we sure as hell couldn't get out!"

I remembered it well.

IV

TALES OF VOICE DISORDERS

In the normal speaking population, we take our voices for granted. Our breathing is adequate to support a normal voice, which always seems to be there for us with adequate loudness, appropriate pitch, and a relatively normal voice quality. The sound of the voice (**phonation**) is produced by actual vibration of the two vocal folds, produced by the outgoing air stream passing between the approximated folds, setting them into vibration. The vibration produces the sound of voice. This is why normal voicing is so dependent on adequate and normal respiration. Severe breathing difficulties make normal voice production impossible. In voice therapy, voice is often improved by better coordination of breathing with the timing of one's speech.

The pitch of the voice is related to the overall size and thickness of the vocal folds. Infants and young children have higher pitched voices related to the relative smallness of their vocal folds. With physical maturity, the larynx and airway become larger and the voice deepens. The pitch of the speaking voice and of the singing voice is directly related to the size of the vibrating vocal folds in the larynx. With laryngeal growth at the time of puberty, the female voice pitch drops about half an octave with the male voice dropping a full octave or more. The resonance of the voice (**quality, nasality**) is determined by the relative openness of the throat, mouth, and nasal passages. Resonance disturbances are often related to infections, allergies, and throat-nasal tissue problems. A voice disorder can be caused by problems of respiration and/or phonation and/

or resonance. The ear-nose-throat physician (**ENT or otolaryngologist**) and the voice clinician (usually a **speech-language pathologist (SLP)**) work closely together in the management of children and adults with voice disorders. Most voice disorders are classified by the ENT or SLP as either **functional** or **organic** in origin. A voice problem that is functional in causation is a faulty voice produced with normal mechanisms in a faulty manner. For example, the young high school cheerleader uses his or her voice without adequate breath support and produces a strain on the vocal cords, resulting in a hoarse voice. With proper voice training, the vocal mechanisms usually can produce a normal voice. An organic voice disorder may be heard in a hoarse, strained voice that is produced by physically altered mechanisms. For example, a vocal fold with a cyst on it will produce a faulty voice. The cyst hinders the quality of voice. After removal of the cyst by the ENT surgeon, with some vocal training following the surgery, the patient may experience a normal voice again. In many voice cases, there is a mixture of functional and organic components. This is why anyone with a voice disorder should have a thorough diagnostic workup <u>before</u> receiving any kind of voice management.

As a voice clinician, it has been my clinical experience that many voice patients with functional voice problems often possess personalities that are a bit hyper. The patients are extroverted, laugh a lot, and are somewhat happy personalities, often somewhat controlling of the people around them. Their voice problems are often related to excessive muscle tension and continual voice usage. In contrast (and this could be a faulty observation), the personality patterns of patients with an organic cause of their voice problem seem to fit in well with the general population. Most voice patients, regardless of the cause of their voice problem, are desperate for help and follow closely the voice regimens developed to help them achieve normal voice.

In the tale, **Signal Light Practice**, we follow the self-practice antics of an attorney with a functional voice problem. The importance of one's voice pitch level in establishing gender identification on the telephone is told in the second voice disorder tale, **I Am My Wife**. The danger of putting a person on "voice rest" is then described in a tale of a seven year old girl who lost her voice completely in **No Talking for Ten Days**. A woman who had her larynx totally removed because of laryngeal cancer tells us that the worst problem she experienced with no voice was being unable to voice her emotions in **I Can't Laugh or Cry**. In **Piano Lessons with Chopin**, we laugh with an older woman with a wandering personality who could never get around to talking about her voice problem. A 44-year old female executive with **A Little Voice** tells us of the difficulty she had expressing authoritative decisions with her "tiny voice." As some laryngectomy patients continue to smoke after total surgical removal of the larynx, a 60 year old maitre d' tells us about his smoking problem in **A Smoky "Good Evening."** These are but a few talking tales with laughter and tears that we have pulled from the files of hundreds of voice patients over the years. For most voice problems, the presenting problem can be minimized, offering little humor or sadness to other observers.

SIGNAL LIGHT PRACTICE

TOM, a 64-year old attorney, continued to develop some hoarseness at the end of the day after having used his voice all day in various professional settings. An otolaryngological examination confirmed that he was experiencing some mild vocal fold swelling, "probably secondary to misuse of his voice." Our clinical voice evaluation found that Tom utilized very little breath support for what he wanted to say, demonstrated some neck and jaw tensions, and generally spoke with abrupt, hard glottal attack. A striking observation found that Tom hardly opened his mouth when he spoke, speaking almost through clenched teeth. To illustrate his closed-mouth talking, we asked him in jest, "Have you ever been a ventriloquist?" When he laughingly said "no" to the question, he got the message of the need to open his mouth more as we replied, "Well, you could be good at it as you rarely open your mouth much when you speak."

∗∗∗

Among the various voice exercises we asked Tom to practice was to open his mouth more as he spoke. We used an old chewing therapy method, where the patient pretends he is chewing up a stack of several crackers with an exaggerated mouth opening while repeating some kind of phrase. We provide him with a nonsense word model, AHLAMETERAH, which he was to say while performing the exaggerated chewing. The sounds of the model enabled him to speak the "word" with an open mouth. His other voice exercises were more conventional, often using some kind of auditory playback equipment.

Because practicing exaggerated chewing makes the patient look ridiculous, it is best done alone. We often recommend that chewing practice while driving the car provides one with an excellent private practice time and place without observers. One must continue repeating the exaggerated movement until it becomes more automatic, resulting in a more conventional mouth movement of lips and jaw while speaking.

Tom did a lot of driving in his work, giving him ample time for chewing practice. He was able to even have fun with the practice. He told us of driving his car while chewing with a wide open mouth, and one day stopping at a signal light, waiting for the signal to turn green. Adjacent to his car on the right was another waiting driver who had looked over at Tom with a startled look and kept staring at him until the light changed to green when he yelled across to Tom, "I don't know what you're on, fellow, but be careful!"

✳✳✳

When Tom told us this story the next week in therapy, we knew that the message of opening one's mouth more when speaking was a talking-rule that he would never forget. Working on better breath control, speaking with an easy onset of words, and letting his voice resonate more fully with a more open mouth all seemed to fuse together, giving Tom a normal voice throughout the day, with a total elimination of voice strain.

VOICE DISORDER TALE 2

I AM MY WIFE

ONE of the more disturbing voice problems one may encounter is speaking at an inappropriate pitch level, with a voice either too low or too high. A man might sound like a woman or a woman may sound like a man. Obviously, this kind of gender confusion can be at its worst while speaking on the telephone. We judge the gender of the people with whom we are speaking, in part, by their voices. Although there is sometimes a physical cause of an excessively low or high voice pitch, it is often something one has learned to do that could be corrected by voice therapy. Thornton was a 51-year old swimming pool maintenance man who came into the voice clinic with an inappropriately high-pitched voice.

***

The referring letter said that while Thornton had always had a higher voice, it became even higher after he inhaled excessive chlorine gas in a swimming pool servicing accident. Four weeks after the incident, he sought help for his voice. When asked at the first interview why he had come to see us, he answered, "I am my wife on the phone and people are beginning to think that she is me." He went on to elaborate that when he answered the phone, his high-pitched voice contributed to his listeners thinking he was his wife. He felt, also, that his wife who had a low-pitched voice was often mistaken for him. Although they laughed at the gender confusion between them and their phone listeners, it was becoming a serious problem for them socially. He wanted help.

A few sessions of voice therapy helped to lower his speaking voice about two full musical notes, although leaving him with a voice that was still well within the adult female range of speaking voices. To sound more masculine in his speech, particularly on the phone, he was encouraged to drop his pitch inflection towards the end of the utterance. In general, men tend to lower their voices at the end of a sentence while women often have a slight rising pitch-inflection. Also, speaking with a crisper, more abrupt speaking manner is heard by listeners as more masculine than feminine. By incorporating both these speaking styles, dropping inflection and speaking with more abrupt word pronunciation, Thornton was able to help his listeners on the phone know that they were speaking to a man. His pitch level, for reasons unknown, never returned lower to pre-accident levels.

✳✳✳

The voice pitch that an adult uses plays a primary role in gender identification, particularly on the telephone where the speaker cannot be seen. Other masculine speaking traits, such as dropping inflection and speaking with abruptness can be added to the phone voice to aid in gender identification. Besides voice pitch and pitch inflections, the loudness of voice and the rate of speech contribute to gender identification. Communication research between the sexes has found in general that men speak a bit louder with a faster rate of speech than women do. When the speaker can be seen in face to face situations, masculine body posture and gestures can also help in accentuating one's gender.

VOICE DISORDER TALE 3

NO TALKING FOR TEN DAYS

PENNY at age seven years did a lot of yelling and a fair amount of crying. By the end of her first year in school in the 1960s, she began to experience severe voice hoarseness. Her parents took her to a Cleveland ENT who found that Penny had "bilateral vocal nodules." Vocal nodules form on the middle of the vibrating muscle of the vocal folds, caused by continuous voice misuse (yelling, screaming, crying, and talking loud.) Nodules are usually found similar in size, somewhat symmetrical, on both vocal folds. Today, it is felt that the best way to get rid of these vocal masses is by counseling and voice therapy, designed to minimize the causative vocal abuse. In the early 1960s, however, nodules were more commonly removed surgically, followed by up to two weeks of complete voice rest in which in time the bilateral surgical sites would heal.

The nodules, one on each vocal fold, were successfully removed for Penny by surgery. To promote healing, the surgeon instructed the parents to do everything they could do to keep Penny quiet (no talking, no crying) for up to two weeks. The parents answered the doctor's request by saying that they would do what they could do, but realized that Penny had always been very active vocally and the "voice rest" requirement would be difficult to enforce. The doctor was very good with Penny in explaining the need for voice rest, and as she left his office, he remarked again, "no talking now for ten days."

***

About two weeks after surgery, the parents brought Penny back for her postoperative examination. They reported that Penny had been very good about not making any vocal noises. In fact, they had not heard voice in the two weeks since the surgery. On examination, the ENT doctor reported that she had very good vocal fold healing and could now "Go ahead and talk, Penny, all you want." The child smiled back, grabbed the doctor's coat, and whispered to him, "I can't find my voice anymore." When the doctor replied, "Let me help you," he made several suggestions, but Penny could only shake her head without making any voice. The family returned home and no matter what they did, the child could not produce voice.

One of the dangers of putting a voice patient on voice rest is that the patient may find other ways to communicate, such as Penny did, by gesture and whisper without the need for voicing. She could only speak in a whisper. Three to four weeks after the nodule surgery, she still had no voice. The ENT surgeon then referred her to our university clinic with this referral notation, "This 7-yr old child had bilateral vocal nodules removed and after a brief voice rest, she has refused to try to talk."

We found Penny to be very cooperative during our testing and therapy, even though her first voicing attempts met with failure. We found that there was some truth to her mother's statement, "Penny seems to have forgotten how to talk." We countered, "She seems eager to talk, but can only do so in a whisper." Her voiceless speech was categorized as **functional aphonia**. We were able to confirm early in our voice evaluation that the child demonstrated a normal cough when asked to do so.

Coughing demonstrates that the vocal folds are not paralyzed and can physically come together. When an individual coughs, the vocal folds are brought firmly together and suddenly parted by an explosive outgoing breath. A firm cough tells the clinician two things: 1) her vocal folds are not paralyzed as they are brought together with firm muscle contractions and 2) the coughing sound can be extended through voice therapy into normal voice. This confirmed the observation that Penny was experiencing a functional aphonia, a voiceless condition not related to organic factors such as paralysis.

I explained to Penny that sometimes when people stopped using their voices after surgery, they had some trouble "getting their voice started again." Voice was kind of like an engine, "it needed a starter to get it going." I was planting for her the "seed" that total voice return would be possible because we knew how to get it started. We were soon able to get Penny to make a light coughing sound, after which I commented, "There, I can hear the vocal folds coming together again. Did you hear that noise when you coughed? That sound was the voice coming off of the vocal folds."

We then showed Penny how to extend a light phonation after the cough. Instead of coughing abruptly, we held onto the cough with an extended voice. We then introduced, "cough---onnnnne." One way for hanging onto voice after the cough was by introducing "one", prolonging its production with a light voice. Penny was thrilled with the voicing of her first word in many weeks. We tempered our reaction to her voice success (it's easy to scare the phonation away with clinician over-reaction.) We spent about ten minutes producing about a dozen monosyllabic words that she could say after the light cough. By the end of our first session, Penny was able to use light voice without need of the precipitating cough, the "cough starter." We kept our voice list short to about fifteen words, demonstrating to her mother how easily she could say them.

We terminated the session after a clinic hour and told Penny to practice the words on the list just as we had done and to do no more than those fifteen. We scheduled her return clinic visit for the next day. However, Penny was so excited by her discovery of her voice that she would not stop practicing that evening. By the time she went to bed, her parents reported that Penny demonstrated a normal voice for whatever she wanted to say. She came in the next morning to our clinic a very happy girl with a normal voice. We celebrated with her and before she left the clinic, we planted another "seed" which often helps the voice patient who may be fearful that his or her voice may be lost again, "Penny, you've found your voice again and it will never, never leave you." In a nine year follow-up for Penny's reactive aphonia after voice rest, the family reported that she had never again lost her voice.

***

Functional aphonia is usually treated effectively by the speech-language pathologist, often requiring only one or two therapy sessions. Methods for restoring phonation include the cough-extension method described for Penny, or using inhalation phonation as a method for finding voice, or asking the patient to whisper-read aloud and then introduce loud masking noise (which will often turn the whisper into actual voice.) Functional aphonia usually has a very favorable outcome, restoration of normal voice.

While voice rest is still used post-surgically with some voice patients, it sometimes results in difficulty retrieving normal voice after the voice rest has ended. It seems like the voice patient has "forgotten" how to phonate. Because of this occasional problem of retrieving voice, it has been my clinical observation that complete voice rest should be avoided after surgery. Instead, we encourage the patient to use a light voice or a "confidential voice", the kind of voice we use in a private conversational situation. Such a light voice does not seem to add any irritation to the vocal folds as they heal after some kind of surgical procedure.

VOICE DISORDER TALE 4

I CAN'T LAUGH OR CRY

ROBERTA, a 54 year old divorced mother of three teenagers, was kidded continuously about her low-pitched voice. She had for years worked in a downtown Denver coffee shop and was able to support her family from alimony monies, wages, and some very good tips. Unfortunately, she had developed a habit of smoking, consuming nearly two packs of cigarettes a day. In her busy life, she was able to balance her mothering duties with church responsibilities and her lunch and evening work as a waitress.

As her hoarse voice deepened in pitch, she also developed an annoying cough. Since waiting on tables limited her ability to cough when she wanted to do so, she did two things: coughed as lightly as possible in public or made frequent trips to the employees' restroom where she could cough heavily enough to clear out offensive mucus. It was her coughing problem, not her deep voice that forced her to seek some medical attention.

The otolaryngologist found that Roberta had extensive cancer of the larynx, severe enough to require the surgical removal of her total larynx **(laryngectomy)**. This would require breathing through a surgically created opening in her neck **(tracheostomy)** plus the need for developing a new substitute voice **(esophageal speech)**. The very day that she was told of her cancer diagnosis, Roberta vowed to quit smoking (and has never had a cigarette since). To help Roberta understand what she was facing, she had several pre-surgical visits from two women who had received the same kind of operation and had made wonderful recoveries. They each spoke to her with their new voices, describing how their family lives and work experience had continued on very well. Their inspirational stories convinced Roberta to proceed with her total laryngectomy, the total removal of her larynx, or voice box.

***

Roberta had a successful laryngectomy operation, followed by some radiation therapy around the operative site. The surgeon helped her develop a new substitute voice by developing an opening between her windpipe and esophagus, and then inserting a small plastic tube through the opening, enabling her outgoing breath to flow into her esophagus. Once in the esophagus, this air can then escape through the esophageal sphincter, the muscle opening at the top of the esophagus. When expired air passes through this tight opening, it produces a burp sound. This is the same mechanism any person uses whenever we belch out air. In the case of the laryngectomy patient, this air-sound is used as a substitute voice. Patients who are good at using this esophageal voice can often say eight to ten words at a time on one continuous belching sound.

With the referral of one of the laryngectomy visitors who had visited Roberta before the operation, she began receiving voice therapy lessons with the speech-language pathologist (SLP). The SLP worked with her to increase the amount of air she could use for vibration of her esophagus. In a few sessions, she was able to say two words at a time, particularly words that began with plosive sounds (p,b,t,d,k,g). Roberta was determined to get back a usable voice that would enable her to return to her work as a waitress. She joked with her voice clinician that her new voice sounded more like a woman, higher in pitch, than her old low voice.

Roberta was invited by several of her new voice friends to attend a laryngectomy support group. Every other week, a group of voice patients met together for an evening of chat and coffee among themselves and family members. Roberta had always had an open gregarious personality, and as soon as she was able to say a few words, she actively participated in group discussions. One evening, she surprised the group when she talked about voice and emotion when she said, "Not having a voice is one thing, but the thing I miss the most with my new burp-voice is that I can't laugh or cry." She went on to say that the laughing voice and the sobbing voice just did not feel the same with her new substitute voice. She said that one way that she had always coped with her family obligations without a husband on the scene, was to shut her bedroom door and then lie down and cry. After sobbing a bit, she felt relieved and able to cope with the family's day to day problems. She missed now not being able to have a normal crying voice.

***

Roberta went on to become one of the best esophageal speakers I had heard in my professional experience. Like the two women who had visited her prior to her surgery, she signed on as a visitor friend to visit new laryngeal cancer patients. She not only became a proficient speaker, but her role as a working mother was exemplary to new patients concerned for their futures after surgery. Although we never forgot her "I can't laugh or cry" comments, she had learned to feel and express those emotions again. Her sensitivity to human needs after surgery made Roberta one of our most valued visitors to see new patients before receiving a laryngectomy.

PIANO LESSONS WITH CHOPIN

O VER the years, I have often noticed new adult voice patients express a need to validate their trust in the voice clinic that they are considering to help them with their problem. They will frequently cite the referring physician's comments that coming to see us will resolve their voice problem or that this clinician "knows what he is doing." The patient wants to express his or her faith in the new voice evaluation and treatment. I will never forget one patient's comments. We'll call her Wanda, a well-dressed woman in her mid-sixties. When I went to pick her up in the waiting room, she stood, extended her hand and said, "Oh, doctor, I'm thrilled to meet you. Having voice therapy with you is like having piano lessons with Chopin."

Her greeting was only the beginning of a most unusual clinic evaluation. The voice clinician working with adult patients will occasionally see a patient similar to Wanda, whose free-flowing personality revealed communication problems far beyond concern for a hoarse voice. Her fun, eccentric, outgoing need to talk made it difficult to conduct any kind of vocal assessment. When we counseled her that voice therapy would not be of as much help as perhaps psychological counseling would be, she embraced the idea of seeing a psychologist when she replied, "Imagine me with a few sessions with Sigmund Freud."

***

A glimpse or two of my voice evaluation attempts with Wanda well illustrate why voice therapy was not possible. As we walked to the clinic office, I asked her why she had come to our voice clinic to see us. She quickly answered in a loud voice, "Oh, doctor, I've been wanting to get after my voice for months now. My bad voice is getting in the way of everything I try to do." This was one of the few mentions of her voice problem in the entire interview. She quickly provided me with a full case history with very little questioning by me required. What was so remarkable about her case, and the reason I have resurrected her dialogue, was the detailed narrative she would provide about bizarre events in her life that seemed to have little relevance to her voice problem.

I asked her, "How does your voice get in the way of the things you want to do?"

She answered promptly, "It's the birds, doctor, it's the birds. Some days they can't hear what I try to tell them."

After telling me that weekly she put out over thirty pounds of bird seed in her backyard for "the birds of Denver," she went on to say that "some of my neighbors did not like me anymore because the birds were always flying over their properties, soiling their roofs, their sidewalks, and their driveways. The birds want to flap their wings and sing their songs of love and happiness. But so many of my neighbors would rather polish their barbecues and scrub their lounge chairs than listen to a thrasher sing." It became quickly apparent that her hobby with the birds had isolated her from her neighbors.

During our one-hour evaluation, Wanda never stopped talking. Another example of her talking can be seen in this tape-recorded segment:

"Doctor, did you ever see a robin have a convulsion?"

"No, I've never seen any kind of bird have a convulsion." I answered.

"Well, it's the pesticides, doctor, that get to them. It hit this dear little robin one Sunday morning, and I go out to the feeder, and he's twitching there looking up at me for help. I held him and did what I could because I knew him. He'd been at our place every spring since I can remember with his whole family. But somehow he got into the neighbor's yard with all his chlordane and other killers and it got to him. I've gone up and down the street talking to the folks that live there to switch to buttermilk. You see, buttermilk is the best pesticide we have because it kills the insects and leaves the squirrels and the birds alone. My robins know that, my doves know it, but that Sunday morning one of my dearest robin friends couldn't get enough to eat at my place, so he drifted over next door or some place and ate their flower poison. By the time, he got back to our sanctuary, the chlordane had hit his darling little brain and he got the convulsion. You could almost see his little brain pulsing to push out the poison. I am sorry to say, he never came out of it."

All attempts that I made to get the patient back to the issue of her voice problem were usually met with other long narratives, generally about her birds, but also about saving the rabbits and the coyotes. Problems with her voice were the least of what concerned her.

***

While Wanda sounded as if she had a voice problem, her overriding problem appeared to be a number of environmental concerns and problems with her neighbors. It was apparent early in our interview that voice therapy designed to curb her excessive talking would not be successful. When it was pointed out to her again that she might profit from talking with a psychologist, she seemed to accept the idea. However, follow-up with her psychologist revealed that after two sessions, Wanda had discontinued further appointments. I met her by chance at a grocery store several years later, and she voiced her concern to me that the organic foods had been contaminated. She warned me by saying something like this, "You sure don't want to buy those organic berries, doctor. You pay more for the organic fruits which are heavier with poisons than the regular fruits, despite the fact that the grocers deny it." Listening to Wanda in the grocery store brought back old memories of our voice evaluation several years before.

VOICE DISORDER TALE 6

A LITTLE VOICE

CATHERINE had worked as a manuscript reader for a major publishing house for about ten years. She had recently been appointed as a senior acquisitions editor whose frequent responsibility was meeting with various authors to discuss manuscript strategies. For a life-time, she had been kidded by others about her baby-sounding, high-pitched voice. Finally, she came to our voice clinic wondering if voice therapy would help her develop a more professional voice to use with her author clients, both on the telephone and in face to face meetings. The baby-sounding voice was quickly apparent as she answered questions during the history-taking part of our evaluation. We explained to her early in our testing that the baby-sounding voice was primarily caused by placing one's tongue too far forward within the mouth.

During our voice evaluation, we were able to confirm by two ways that Catherine carried her tongue too far forward in her mouth: 1) when videotaping her mouth as she spoke, we could observe a lot of forward tongue; and 2) lateral x-ray imaging confirmed excessive front-of-the-mouth tongue carriage as she spoke. We also found that her voice pitch was significantly higher (just below middle C4) than that of most women her age (G3). We scheduled her for individual voice therapy.

✳✳✳

It did not appear that the higher voice pitch contributed much to the baby-sound of her voice. Therefore, we placed therapy emphasis on what we call "voice focus," where the voice seems to have a resonance focus. A normal voice sounds like it is coming from the middle-top of one's mouth, almost sounding as if it were resonating from the surface of one's tongue. We explained to Catherine that there are four main resonance deviations in voice focus: 1) too far forward; 2) excessively back in the throat; 3) down low behind the tongue in the base of the throat, or 4) nasal focus with voice coming out of the nose. We told Catherine that in therapy we would begin by developing back throat focus, the very opposite of what she showed us when producing her baby voice. In the beginning of therapy, we practiced making the back sounds of English, /ka/ and /ga/. These two sounds are made with the tip of the tongue down in the front of the mouth with the posterior tongue body arched high up against the roof (palate) of the mouth. We used an immediate playback recorder for her to say back sounds (/k/ and /g/) and then hear an immediate playback of what she had just said. We recorded her producing a few /k/ and /g/ sounds in a series like "kuh-kuh-kuh"---"kah-kah-kah"---"guh-guh-guh"---"gah-gah-gah." Producing these back sounds immediately got rid of her baby resonance, replacing it with full posterior resonance which we called for her a "big voice."

Catherine was surprised and thrilled that in the first few moments of voice therapy she was able to produce and immediately hear her self producing a back voice. We cautioned her that the back voice was a "means to an end." We would use the back voice focus only temporarily. Eventually, we would work on lowering her voice pitch but our beginning therapy would focus on producing appropriate voice focus, giving her an immediately more pleasant voice. She required practice with the back voice before we proceeded to bring the voice to a normal, more forward position. We also discussed that the "front voice" and the "back voice" were only imagery concepts, not factual absolutes; that is, voice seems to resonate more forward or backward in the mouth. Before the next therapy session, she reported back to us that she had never stopped practicing the series of /k/ and /g/ sounds.

She found driving the car, also, a good place to practice, and whenever she found herself alone, she found great joy in using the back voice sounds.

In subsequent voice therapy sessions, we practiced repeating at different loudness levels individual /k/ and /g/ words like, "comb, come, corn, gone, gun, gum." She would record her voice on a playback recorder [the Facilitator] and listen immediately on playback to her back voice productions. After a hundred percent success producing back words, she advanced to reading sentences heavily loaded with /k/ and /g/ sounds. Catherine remained highly motivated in therapy and had eventually an easy time bringing her voice "more forward" to normal resonance levels. She could read aloud maintaining good resonance focus, avoiding extremes in both anterior and posterior tongue carriage. At the last therapy session, even her conversation was completely free of the baby voice that she had when she started therapy.

✳✳✳

We have continued to talk to Catherine by phone over a number of years, and we always hear a normal voice. Catherine recently told us, "I can still remember the awful baby voice that I had. It never seemed to match the responsibilities that I had in my publishing world. I can now use my voice to serve me." Getting rid of her anterior voice focus was a wonderful example of success using symptomatic voice therapy. We ignored working only to lower her pitch and worked instead on changing her voice resonance, using excessive posterior resonance to help her eliminate excessive anterior tongue posturing, the primary cause of her little voice.

A Smoky Good Evening

A throat cancer patient may have to have his or her larynx (voice box) removed surgically. Such patients then develop a substitute voice either by belching up air from the esophagus which sounds like a hoarse voice, or by placing a small electric instrument against the neck, resulting in an instrument vibration that sounds like a mechanical voice. Such patients breathe through a hole in their neck, which permits air to flow in and out of their lungs. Unlike a normal throat that allows both air and food to pass through together before separating to either the lungs or the stomach, patients with a larynx removed (**laryngectomy**) have breathing and eating as separate anatomic functions. All breathing (inspiration and expiration of air) passes through the opening in the neck (**tracheostomy**). Whatever contents are in the mouth can be swallowed and diverted down the esophagus into the stomach.

***

Harvey was a maître d' for many years at one of Cleveland's finest restaurants. Even after he had throat cancer necessitating a laryngectomy followed by voice training, he went back to work with his new voice and resumed greeting patrons at the door when they entered the restaurant.

After his operation, he still liked to smoke, but now found conventional smoking almost impossible. He'd either have to place the cigarette directly in the neck opening (which he found most unpleasant) or derive a little tobacco taste by attempting to inhale through his lips. Since his mouth was surgically disconnected from his airway and lungs, the smoke that gathered in his mouth could not be inhaled and would often be swallowed down into his stomach. One of Harvey's favorite stories to tell after his laryngectomy was of a night at work

when he forgot to empty his stomach of smoke. On a break from his maître d'
duties, he went to the employees' lounge to enjoy a menthol cigarette. He had
found that a menthol cigarette felt better in the back of his throat than conventional cigarettes. He smoked the cigarette down, swallowing much of its smoke
into his stomach. Usually after smoking this way, he remembered to belch up
the smoke before he began talking to anyone. This particular night, he forgot
to belch out the smoke trapped in his stomach, and he returned directly to his
entrance post at the restaurant. Harvey pleasantly greeted two couples that came
into the restaurant. He gave them a big smile and said, "Good evening. Ah, a
table for four. Won't you please come this way?" With each word of his belch-
supported voice, smoke puffs came out of his mouth. Harvey said that he would
never forget the startled looks on their faces as he greeted them. As he led them
to their requested nonsmoking table, he was amazed that with such a smoky
greeting they would follow him any place, let alone to a nonsmoking table.

✳✳✳

This story took place a little over fifty years ago. Now that smoking has been
found to have such a direct relationship to laryngeal cancer, very few laryngecto-
mees continue today to "swallow-smoke" as Harvey did. For those few patients
without a voice box who still take in smoke through their mouths and into
the stomach, the smoke will remain in the stomach until it is belched out, or
contrary to some rumors of how the smoke finally exits, smoke will eventually be
absorbed through the lining of the intestines.

V

TALES OF SPEECH PATHOLOGY

Speech pathology is a most fascinating profession. I discovered it by accident. After being discharged from the US Army in 1947, I had four years of college available on the GI Bill, but I could only begin my studies as a general liberal arts college student. I had not decided what kind of work that I might want to do for a life-time. I was interested in acting, writing, broadcasting, social work, psychology, and possibly medicine. As a junior at the University of Redlands in California, I became a speech major with an emphasis given to radio/television with a minor study area in clinical psychology. Regardless of one's specialization interests, a course in communication disorders was required in the junior year for all speech majors. Any kind of problem in talking was new to me, as I had always experienced good success in speaking and enjoyed entertaining listeners with vocal imitations of well-known actors, singers, and politicians. Until that course in communication disorders, I had only random exposure to people who had problems in listening and talking.

Our speech pathology professor, William R. Parker, had completed his doctoral studies at the University of Southern California under the direction of Lee E. Travis. Both Drs. Parker and Travis that particular year (1949) taught the communication disorders course, with heavy emphasis on stuttering and the possible psychological problems experienced by the children and adults who stuttered. I found their course in speech pathology appealing to me as it combined information on social, psychological, and medical issues. Before the course ended that semester, I had switched my major to speech pathology-audiology. In the subsequent year and a half of undergraduate study, I became absorbed in such topics as brain and cerebral function, the differences between neurotic and psychotic behavioral patterns, and the cause(s) of stuttering and its treatment. Upon graduation, I was hoping to work in some clinical setting with people who experienced the problem of stuttering.

Through a series of unexpected events after graduation, I was hired as a "Language Retraining Instructor" in the Aphasia Clinic of the Long Beach Veterans Hospital, California. At that time (1951), this Clinic was one of three aphasia centers designated by the Veterans Administration for WWII and Korean War veterans returning home with the problem of aphasia. Fortunately, with close supervision and my psychology background, I think I soon developed as a competent and understanding speech-language pathologist. Some of the aphasia tales in Chapter I of this book came from that first clinical experience in Long Beach in the early 1950s. I soon realized that my educational background was too limited if I wanted to succeed in a life-career as a speech pathologist. After two years at the VA, I searched for a doctoral program. Applying at 14 graduate programs, I fortunately ended up in Cleveland, Ohio, at Western Reserve University (now Case-Western Reserve). I experienced a five year graduate program that provided diverse but advanced study in stuttering, neurogenic communication problems, psychopathology, and voice disorders.

One of my first post-doctoral clinical jobs was directing a clinical program in stuttering at the Cleveland Hearing and Speech Center. The first two speech pathology tales came out of that experience. **Pith Helmet Therapy** tells briefly of a unique therapy approach with a five-year old boy who stuttered so badly that he had no functional speech. We look then at the fear of stuttering experienced by a Great Lakes ship captain who described the power of both negative and positive thinking in **I Can Pa-Pa-Pa-Park a Ship.** In the earlier days of the speech pathology profession, it was not uncommon for persons who stuttered to choose speech pathology as their career profession. In **Pick Us Up in**

the Morning, I describe an unforgettable visit to a graduate program in speech pathology headed by a person who was also a severe stutterer.

Playing the role of a speech-language pathologist (SLP) in a medical setting presents many of the challenges and observations we have described in the first four sections of this volume. Beyond my clinical role as a SLP, as one gained more experience within the profession, there are increased opportunities for professional travel, visiting other programs nationally and internationally. The remaining tales in this **Section 5** tell with humor some of the unique situations I encountered in my professional travels. Speech pathology is often difficult to explain to people out of the profession. I describe a difficult situation explaining speech therapy to hospital visitors in **Two Minutes, Daniel.** SLP speakers (the experts from out of town) often encounter severe auditory and visual limitations from their speaking arenas as experienced in **The L-Shaped Atrium.** The unbelievable travel obstacles I experienced attempting to present a voice workshop in Minnesota are recalled in **The Workshop in Duluth.** One of my most unforgettable SLP adventures I ever experienced was visiting the Kansas State Penitentiary. I have for a life-time wondered what happened to the unfortunate young man with whom I visited in **The State Penitentiary**.

A well-known fellow speech-language pathologist and I made a site-accreditation visit to a clinical program in Pennsylvania. To get there, we flew to Philadelphia and then spent over an hour and a half in a "stop in every town" airport limousine. After completing the site-visit, we asked our hosts if there were a faster way to return back to the Philadelphia airport. They suggested that we take a local charter flight back. In **Are You the Boys Flying to Philly?**, we take a fun look back (it was <u>not</u> fun at the time) at the harrowing flight in the Cessna and the pilot who flew us.

PITH HELMET THERAPY

OUR professional understanding of the problem of stuttering seems to evolve over time. Normal speech is characterized by a fluent flow of words. Stuttering begins often with a breakdown in this fluent flow, called a dysfluency, with the individual repeating the first sound of a word that he or she is attempting to say. Or the whole word may be repeated at the beginning of an utterance. The repetition may then develop into a prolongation of the first sound of a word, or prolonging the vowel in the middle of the word one wants to say. Or the dysfluency may evolve further with the person not able to say the desired sound, often pursing the lips to speak but not able to produce any sound or word. In the speech pathology treatment of stuttering, the open repeating of a whole word is a much better prognosticator than the complete blocking of a sound or not being able to initiate a spoken word. The young boy we present here had a complete blocking of his attempts at speech.

Ronnie, age five, was the most severe stutterer I had ever seen. When he tried to talk, he would purse his mouth to say something but no sound would come out. He was the second child of two severe stutterers who had met in a midwestern university stuttering program. The parents, because of their own lifetime speech struggles, had early concerns about Ronnie's word repetitions which had started before he was three years old. However, they waited until he was five before bringing him for a speech evaluation.

* * *

At the time of my evaluation, Ronnie could not initiate saying a single word. When I asked him his name, he spent two minutes trying to tell me. Attempting to speak, he would purse his lips, hold his breath, close his eyes, contort his

face, and make a few unintelligible grunts. On physical examination, we found
his voice box (larynx), throat, tongue, and lips to be normal, fully capable of
producing normal speech. He was tested and found to have normal hearing. He
could follow directions quickly and perform well on non-verbal cognitive tasks,
indicating that he had good, if not superior intelligence. His problem in communication was his severe stuttering. He could not talk.

In trying to think of something Ronnie could say without struggle, I thought
that perhaps he would be able to repeat nonsense sounds after me. So I conceived
the idea of "jungle talk," as if we were repeating the sounds of jungle natives. We
each wore a jungle hat or pith helmet to create a speaking environment totally
different for Ronnie (a situation I now call fondly "pitch helmet therapy.") I
told him, "Instead of using real words, we'll pretend we're in a jungle in India.
We'll meet people who speak a different language than we do. When they speak
their different words, like 'wagga porpa' (which I said in a loud voice), we'll say
'wagga porpa' right after them. You put on a jungle hat, Ronnie," I said, offering
him a pith helmet. I then put on a pith helmet and we looked at each other in a
mirror, each wearing our jungle hats, and I said, "You'll be able say jungle to talk,
Ronnie. You say after what I say."

He looked at me quizzically as he wasn't too sure that this was going to work.
So I said, "Let's try it. When I speak jungle, you say it back to me."

I made up pretend jungle words and said, "goggle-babba."

Ronnie answered me quickly, "goggle-babba." He looked very surprised and
pleased, as this was probably the first utterance in some time that he had been
able to say without struggle.

We quickly added more jargon words and just as quickly he would repeat
them back to me, showing no facial grimace and no sign of stuttering. After
five minutes of his repeating nonsense words after me, Ronnie gave me his own
jargon words, asking me to repeat what he said. We spent the rest of the session,
modeling nonsense sounds and repeating them after one another.

* * *

We wore the pith helmets and did our "jungleeze" repetitions for several
therapy sessions. Since what we were saying had no actual form or meaning,
Ronnie could willingly repeat it back without any evaluation as to whether he
was speaking right or wrong. We used the fluency he had experienced in saying

the jungle sounds as a means of establishing what normal speech fluency might feel like. I subsequently worked with Ronnie on his stuttering for several years with good results. As he said years later as a teenager, looking back at our first sessions together, "That time we did that jungle talk wearing those pith helmets was the first time I ever felt happy using my mouth to say anything." Repeating the nonsense jungle words opened up his ability to use his breath and voice in a speech-like manner.

Ronnie is now in late middle age and most of the time he speaks normally, experiencing only occasional stuttering when in a stressful situation. In a recent conversation with him about this book, he wanted me to now tell this jungle sounds story of when he was a little boy.

SPEECH PATHOLOGY TALE 2

I CAN PA-PA-PA-PARK A SHIP

STUTTERING is generally recognized when an individual repeats a sound as he or she speaks, or prolongs a sound, or gets stuck on a word and cannot seemingly "push" it out. That is the stuttering that we hear. A hidden part of the disorder is that stutterers (the people who stutter) live in extreme fear that they are going to stutter. The anticipation of the stuttering seems to help bring the speech disorder about. Stutterers tell us that they soon "know" when they are going to stutter. They then try to avoid those situations in which the stuttering may occur. Therefore, successful speech therapy for stuttering not only requires modifying the stuttering (repetition, prolongation, or block of words), but it also must include counseling that can aid the stutterer in reducing the fear of stuttering and the anticipation of situations where stuttering usually occurs. Eric, a fifty-year old stutterer and third-generation Great Lakes ship captain, well illustrates the "knowing I'm going to stutter" aspect of the disorder.

* * *

Each year in the winter months, when the Great Lakes were frozen and closed to sea shipping, Eric participated in a weekly adult stuttering group. Eric was a colorful sea captain who liked to tell ship stories, despite his severe stuttering which at times made his story-telling difficult. For the majority of the time in the group, however, he would speak normally without stuttering. Suddenly, for reasons that no one could predict, he would stutter with no word able to come out as he held his breath, tightened his lips, froze his jaw in a fixed position, distorted his face, and closed his eyes. When asked why he would block so in his speech he answered, "When certain ideas or topics come up, I know I am going to stutter---and I do."

His remark about knowing he was going to stutter led to a group discussion about anticipation of stuttering, with most group members telling how they try to avoid situations where they <u>know</u> they will stutter. The group agreed that negative thinking will often produce negative results. Fear of stuttering seems to make stuttering happen. The group leader countered that the same thing is true of positive thinking, which often leads to positive outcomes. Knowing and predicting that one will be successful, like putting a golf ball in the cup or selling one's daily quota, seems to be the first step in successfully doing the task.

Eric well illustrated negative and positive anticipation for the group when he said, "When I have to give my na-na-name to someone, I know I'm going to have t-t-t-trouble. And I always stutter. But, hell, take my work for instance. I can stand on the bridge of my 400 foot freighter, which is longer than a football field, and bring her right up to the docking pier. With her lateral thrusters, I know I can park her right within her assigned berth space. I know I can pa-pa-pa-park a ship. And I do."

✳ ✳ ✳

Much of the stuttering behavior we see and hear comes about, in part, because the individual knows he or she is going to stutter. This same sureness about a negative outcome seems to help make the negative result occur. If Eric, like other people who stutter, could replace the negative expectation that stuttering will occur with positive thoughts that he will speak fluently, one might predict that he would enjoy more fluent speech.

Note: Eric's comment on the last statement above: "That's easy for a normal speaker to say."

Pick Us Up in the Morning

S EVERE stuttering often occurs in particular situations. This is a story of a professional man who stuttered so badly on the telephone that he was often unable to produce a single word, but he talked with near normal fluency in face-to-face communication. Adults with a life-time of stuttering behind them are often conditioned to anticipate that in a particular speaking situation, they are likely to experience an increase in stuttering symptoms. A particular situation might be when attempting to say one's name, or speaking to an authority figure, or talking on the telephone. The more focal the speaking situation (such as introducing one's self), the greater the possibility of a stuttering occurrence.

Early in the development of speech pathology as a profession, it was not uncommon for a person with a life-time history of stuttering to become a speech pathologist. Having experienced personal difficulties talking, such men and women made excellent, sensitive clinicians. Some became speech pathologists in the schools, some went into medical settings, and some migrated to university teaching jobs. This particular tale is about a university professor who stuttered and was also the department head of a university audiology and speech pathology training program. The identities of both the university and the department head have obviously been omitted.

***

In the early 1980s, I served as an accreditation visitor to a number of clinical training programs in speech pathology. Procedures developed by the American Speech-

Language-Hearing Association (ASHA) required training programs in speech pathology and audiology to be re-certified every few years. To do this, a trio of ASHA members would typically make a site visit to the program where they would interview both faculty and students, review course offerings, look at clinical records, and draw conclusions relative to the adequacy of clinical supervision. These visitations were long before the instant convenience of email, requiring in those days an intensive postal and telephone exchange in preparation for the visit. The stay usually required two nights: the first night the team reviewed the program's submitted application; the next full day, the trio visited the program on site, followed that evening by writing their report; early the next morning, the visitors discussed their findings with the department head. The trio of visitors generally left for the airport around noon or early afternoon. The host institution generally made motel/hotel reservations for the three visitors, with each visitor making his or her own travel arrangements.

I was appointed by ASHA to head the site team visiting University X. Each of the three of us arrived at the city airport at different times with each of us finding our own way to the designated motel near the university. Upon arrival at my motel, I spent some time reviewing the materials this training program had submitted to ASHA. I was most impressed with the thoroughness of the documents. When the other two visitants arrived at the motel, it was my duty to call the program head and arrange for him or someone in his department to pick the three of us up in the morning.

I dialed the home number of Dr. Y. His wife answered and I said, "This is Dr. Boone, the ASHA visitor to your husband's program. I 'd like to speak with John."

"Oh, yes, Doctor Boone, he has been expecting your call. Just a moment."

"OK, thank you," I replied. I waited for 10 or 15 seconds, when I heard a noise on the line. I said, "Is this Dr. Y? This is Dan Boone and our site visitors have all arrived."

"Wun-wun-wun-wun-wun." He repeated what sounded like great struggle, and I realized for the first time that he was stuttering.

I interrupted his repetitions and said, "This is Doctor Boone and our site team has arrived at the Holiday Inn. We're very impressed with your accreditation application."

"Wun-wun-wun-wun-wun."

I then hoped to get a message to him, beyond our first greeting. "We'd like you to pick us up in the morning at eight o'clock."

"Wun-wun-wun." The sound of his voice sounded a bit more relaxed and seemed to sound like an agreement.

I wasn't completely sure that he had received my request so I added, "Will you then, John, pick us up at the Holiday after we've had our breakfast. We'll be at the front door at eight o'clock."

"Aaah, ooo, OK."

It sounded like he got the message so I said before hanging up, "OK, we'll look forward to seeing you in the morning."

* * *

John arrived the next morning in his station wagon at the front door of the Holiday Inn promptly at eight o'clock. In our one-to-one greetings and follow-up conversations, he was most personable and showed only occasional word blocks. Our site visit went very well. His excellent application matched all of our observations. I was impressed with his ability to speak with us all day with relatively normal speech. I confirmed that his severe stuttering was primarily on the telephone when I called him in the evening to talk about the next day's schedule, and I again experienced the same "wun" repetitions.

I have never forgotten this site visit event. I had never realized until that time that there could be such a disparity in fluency between complete blockage on the phone and relatively gifted verbal abilities in "live" conversation.

About ten years later, I had a beer with John at an ASHA Convention. He confessed to me his extreme embarrassment in not being able to speak on the phone at the time of our site visit. That particular difficulty talking on the phone on our visit prompted him to receive successful operant speech therapy. He was eventually able to condition away his expectancy to stutter while talking on the phone. In a recent telephone conversation with him about including his story in this book, he spoke with near normal fluency.

SPEECH PATHOLOGY TALE 4

TWO MINUTES, DANIEL

AS part of my clinical training for a Master's degree in speech pathology, I was assigned to Highland View Hospital in Cleveland, Ohio. Highland View in the early 1950s had two clinical populations: 150 custodial care patients and about 175 rehabilitation patients, most of whom had chronic neurogenic impairments. As a graduate student, I spent about 18 hours a week there working as a speech pathologist with patients with aphasia or motor speech problems secondary to such neurological diseases as multiple sclerosis, stroke, Parkinson's disease, amyotrophic lateral sclerosis (ALS), or cerebral palsy. With many of these neurological patients, we worked on improving speech intelligibility and helping some patients to improve swallowing function.

My doctoral dissertation research was conducted at Highland View, selecting subjects randomly from a pool of 125 post-stroke patients who had either right or left sided paralysis (hemiplegia.) After receiving my Ph.D. in 1958 from Western Reserve University, I headed up the speech pathology-audiology program at Highland View. Our section in communication disorders was called Speech Therapy {ST} and was one of four programs (together with Physical Therapy [PT], Occupational Therapy [OT], and Vocational Training [VT]) under the aegis of the Department of Physical Medicine and Rehabilitation {PM&R[, headed at that time by a well known physiatrist, Dr. P.

* * *

In the late 1950s, it was important for our profession to maintain its independence from medicine. ASHA wanted the patient referred to the ST program for evaluation and therapy if indicated, with the speech pathologist planning the appropriate treatment. It was different for physician referrals required for both PT and OT in our PM&R Department. Dr. P. and his assistant physicians would see the patient directly and then prescribe what needed to be done in both PT and OT. Patients with communication disorders were referred by hospital physicians directly to us with the prescription usually reading either "Speech Evaluation and Therapy, if Indicated" or to our staff audiologist for "Hearing Evaluation."

Dr. P. and I worked out the referral steps very well. With a little explanation and a few examples supplied by me, Dr. P. supported the ASHA position. In time, our Speech Therapy staff included me as Director, two full-time speech pathologists (in the 1950s we were not yet called "speech-language pathologists") and a half-time audiologist.

For the few years I worked there in my first post-doctoral position, I wanted to please the man who had employed me, Dr. P. He had been, also, most cooperative and helpful working my work schedule around my doctoral classes and helping me develop the pool of hemiplegic patients for the selection of research subjects. Out of this loyalty, I never complained about the continued stress Dr. P. might put me under when he would unexpectedly ask me to demonstrate a patient to hospital staff or to speak to a group of visitors to Highland View.

The PM&R program at Highland View in the 1950s was well recognized nationally and internationally as a prototype program in rehabilitation medicine. Before coming to this country from Poland shortly after World War II, Dr. P. was well known in Europe for his recognized programs in rehabilitation. Consequently, we had many foreign visitors to our program. Usually without any prior warning, Dr. P. would come into our speech waiting room with five or six visitors or more. Instead of letting me know who they were and where they were from, Dr. P. would typically say, "Doctor Boone is the head of our speech and hearing clinic."

I would quickly take my cue and give the group a "welcome, please come in."

Dr. P. then might say, "Doctor Boone will now tell you how speech therapy fits in for the patients in the Department. You have *two minutes, Daniel.*"

At that particular time in my life, I was able to give a brief but fluent summary about what speech pathology services were all about. If any of our staff were present, I would introduce them. A speech patient was often in the waiting area, and I would introduce them to the visitors. All introductions were included in the time block I now fondly designate as "*Two minutes, Daniel.*"

Dr. P. would stand with the visitors, and look at his watch. When the two-minute designation had expired, Dr. P. would promptly say, "Very well (his frequent statement), and thank you, Daniel," as he then escorted the visitors to his next proud site in the PM&R Department.

* * *

I look back longingly at those days in the late 50s at Highland View Hospital in Cleveland, Ohio. Our speech pathologists there had remarkable impact on improving the lives and communication function of many patients. The positive outcome for many patients we saw there provided me clinical insights I have been able to use for a clinical life-time. And the man who made it all possible for me was Dr. P. I have called him Dr. P. in this brief story because his last name (Peszczynski) was always difficult for me to spell. I did shed fond tears at his memorial service some forty years ago.

THE L-SHAPED ATRIUM

WHEN one travels out of town to deliver a speech or present a workshop, you play the role of the "out of town expert." Over the years, I presented papers or workshops on such topics as cerebral dominance, therapy scoring, aphasia, voice disorders, and transgender communication. I was often the guest of state associations, therapy groups, and medical organizations, both nationally and internationally. I often did not know in advance the room situation in which I would be speaking, how many would be in attendance, audio-visual equipment availability, and whether I would have amplification or not. This is a tale of the worst speaking situation that I can remember.

* * *

Many years ago I was invited by the Louisiana Speech and Hearing Association to present a short course at its annual convention, held that particular year in New Orleans. This was many years before PowerPoint presentations, which then required a separate request by the speaker for a slide projector, screen, a reel-to-reel audiotape recorder, a VHS video playback recorder and monitor(s), laser pointer, and a podium mike/amplifier. I had made appropriate requests through the LSHA organizer and put my advance efforts into organizing the lecture and the auditory/visual playback presentation.

I always enjoyed a visit to New Orleans which usually included going the first night to two jazz venues, sitting through a couple of sets at Preservation Hall and then closing the night with some welcome jazz at Pete Fountain's. I enjoyed the music that night with a few friends and thought little about the three-hour voice therapy short course I would be presenting the next morning.

My particular LSHA presentation was scheduled in the old Sugar Bowl stadium (long before the Louisiana Super Dome was built.) I arrived at the massive stadium a half hour before my presentation was to begin, hopefully to set up the AV equipment and familiarize myself with the room. One of my hostesses led me to where I was to speak, and I could not believe the room to which I had been assigned, a large room that could accommodate an audience of several hundred people. The room was an L-shaped room tucked outside under the slanting seats of the stadium. The room basically had no ceiling but an atrium that reached high above us, probably all he way until it reached the seats in row 40! It appeared to be an acoustic disaster with the possibility of losing sound up into the atrium.

I soon realized that neither my slides or my video could be seen by everyone. It was a massive L-shaped room. Even though the podium had been set up at one end of the L, it seemed that more people could hear and see better if the podium were set at the inner angle were the two L-walls came together. So, we had the podium moved to the middle with the seats set in a V-configuration on each side of the podium facing each other. The television monitors and slide screen were moved centrally, which we felt would allow at least 70 percent of the audience to see the visual presentations.

As the LSHA members began to come in and find their seats, we attempted to do a sound check. The microphone was now central in the room at the lower point of the V. The audio speakers faced each other. We immediately experienced the loss of sound floating up to the atrium. There also seemed to be some competing noise coming from the outside hallway.

As I began speaking much of what I said, even though amplified, seemed to vanish above us. Attempts at increasing loudness produced some reverberation between competing speakers above me on each side of the L-room. People seated within 30 feet of the podium could see and hear without too much difficulty. Beyond that distance from the podium, much of my presentation was lost. Some attendees, who couldn't see or hear the presentation, left the room early. For the presenter (me), it was a nightmare experience that lasted for three hours. For most of the short course, I turned off the amplification and did what I could to project a louder voice. That seemed to improve the sound situation. It took me a day or two to recover my normal voice.

* * *

I learned from that frustrating experience in New Orleans the importance of room selection. Hotel and convention center speaking experiences are often scheduled in rooms that may compete with the presenters and their auditory and visual presentations. Those of us who host conferences should not be shy in demanding that the presentation setting be workable to both the presenter and the audience. Today, with generations of people raised in a loud amplified world, our audiences have real difficulty listening in less than optimum settings.

THE WORKSHOP IN DULUTH

A S frustrating as the speaking circumstances were in The L-Shaped Atrium, nothing can match the travel difficulties I experienced as a scheduled workshop presenter one February day long ago in Duluth, Minnesota. My home was in Denver at the time, and I had not hesitated to schedule a winter voice workshop in Minnesota. I was used to snow and cold weather during the occasional storms that would come over the Colorado mountains into Denver. On the particular night I was scheduled to fly non-stop on Western Airlines from Denver to Minneapolis, the flight was delayed more than two hours. A severe snowstorm had grounded all Denver aviation for several hours. The flight delay gave me several hours to go over my notes, my slides, and the written summaries of several videos I would be presenting the next afternoon in Duluth. My presentation review in the Denver airport was the last event under my complete control for the next few days.

* * *

My plane landed in Minneapolis around one-thirty in the morning. After claiming my luggage, I ventured out to the curb to find some kind of transportation to my airport motel. The digital temperature gauge outside the airport registered fifteen degrees below zero. While waiting for a cab, I experienced icicles forming in my nose, blocking the normal passage of air. I literally could blow out small tapered icicles, and breathe normally for a few minutes before the ice again closed my nostrils. I waited about fifteen minutes before a cab came and delivered me "half-frozen" to my motel.

The next morning I ventured to the airport rental car lot, as I had planned to drive the approximate 150 miles to Duluth, where I would find the Duluth

School Headquarters Building, the site of my afternoon workshop. The rental car was plugged into a "block heater", and since I had never before used such a heater to keep the engine from freezing after parking, the rental personnel showed me how to plug in the parking lot heater when I reached my destination. The car was equipped with metal stud snow tires and after reviewing the highway map with the rental staff, they felt that I would have no difficulty driving on the four lane highway to Duluth.

The highway had been plowed, and there were continuing mounds of the plowed snow stacked (sometimes higher than fifteen feet) along the outside lanes. It started to rain, producing an instant layering of ice. To secure better traction, I remembered how we drove in Colorado mountain snows, keeping the car's right wheels pushed against the ploughed snow piles, providing the vehicle needed traction. Every now and then, the car would hit an icy patch and I would experience some fish-tail swirling on the highway. In contrast to my driving struggles, I remember hearing and seeing a northbound passenger train streaking along side the highway on its uninterrupted rush to Duluth. The ice-snow combination delayed my Duluth arrival about ninety minutes later than I had planned. By consulting my map and by asking directions at a gas station or two, I found the Duluth School Headquarters Building.

I found the parking lot on one side of the building. It had stopped raining by then with a light snow falling. I could spot the vertical block heaters spaced every two open spaces in the parking lot. I parked the car in the lot, placing the space heater on top of the engine block. Since my watch told me the workshop was to begin in about 30 minutes, I forgot about finding a lunch somewhere. All of the workshop materials fit nicely in my Italian leather attaché case, which stepping around the drifts of snow, I carried to the front door. Posted on the door was this notice: THIS BUILDING IS CLOSED. BECAUSE OF THE ICE STORM, THE BOONE VOICE WORKSHOP HAS BEEN CANCELLED.

I realized why the parking lot was nearly empty.

* * *

These were the days before computer generated email and cell phones. There was no way that my hosts could have reached me in Minneapolis. After finding a diner and almost a four-hour wintry drive back to Minneapolis, I reached the airport car rental agency. I had a ten o'clock night flight scheduled back to

Denver. To make my disappointing day complete, my return Western Airlines flight to Denver was cancelled. I was able to find a room again in the same motel, returning back to Denver the next day.

* * *

A few years later at a benefit luncheon in Denver, I met by accident Robert Six, President of Western Airlines, and I enjoyed telling him briefly about my trip to Duluth and his late and cancelled flights. I was more interested, however, in meeting his famous wife, the celebrated Broadway singing star, Ethel Merman.

THE STATE PENITENTIARY

CONSULTING in speech pathology can take the professional to many different settings. One setting that I will always remember in the mid-1960s was the Kansas State Penitentiary (KSP) in Lansing, Kansas. I was asked by a neurologist at the University of Kansas Medical Center to evaluate a KSP inmate who had just acquired a sudden inability to speak, "possibly an expressive aphasia."

∗ ∗ ∗

My only referral information was the patient's name (we'll call him "Carl") and a brief description of the young man's medical problem. Apparently, while undergoing an examination in the prison hospital for a bladder infection, Carl suddenly lost consciousness. Upon awakening, he had no speech and was tentatively diagnosed as having "expressive aphasia."

It was a short but confusing drive from Kansas City, Kansas, north to the KSP in Lansing. Lansing is adjacent to Leavenworth, Kansas, which houses the large federal prison, the U.S Penitentiary at Leavenworth, and several other smaller prisons. I found it somewhat confusing following the signage to be sure I arrived at the correct Kansas prison. Near the prison entrance, I made the mistake of parking my car in a yellow zone not far from the entry gates. As I got out of the car, I heard several cries of "halt," followed by "state your purpose." I then saw on the roof of the two-story entrance building two armed guards pointing their rifles at me. "State your purpose," one of them yelled again..

I yelled back, "I am Doctor Daniel Boone, and I've come to exam a patient in your hospital." (I realized immediately that my historical name might well work against me.)

"You can't park there, doctor. You'll have to drive over to Special Visitors Parking. We'll have guard escorts there to meet you."

I drove by the front entrance and parked in a small lot marked, SPECIAL VISITORS PARKING. As I was getting out of the car, two armed guards approached me, and one of them requested, "Let's see your Special Parking Pass."

"I don't have any special permit, but I have been asked by the Warden to exam a prisoner who has lost his speech." Neither guard interrupted me, so I continued, "My name is Doctor (as long as I said 'doctor' I figured they would think that I was a legitimate visitor) Boone. I've come to see Carl ------ in the prison hospital."

Both men answered, "We can't let you in without a special permit, and we cannot let you park here, either." Taking a two-way radio off of his hip, one guard said, "Tell me your name again and we'll call it in."

"Daniel Boone. I'm a speech doctor."

After what seemed to be many minutes of waiting and hearing them making fun of my name, the guard told me, "We can issue a 411 that'll cover your car, and Carleton here," pointing to the other guard, "can take you to the main post."

Carleton and I walked to the main gate of the Kansas State Penitentiary, where we were met by several other guards. As the guards accompanied me to the warden's office, we walked through a series of clanging metal gates that would lift upward as we would walk under them to the next gate. The whole scene reminded me of an old George Raft movie. I was impressed with how difficult it was to access the warden's office from the inside, thinking how impossible it would be to escape back through the corridors we had just entered.

The prison doctor was waiting for me inside the warden's office along with the warden himself. Both men reviewed Carl's history with the doctor elaborating, "We examined his bladder by inserting a catheter in his penis. The minute the tube got in there, the boy keeled over in a deep faint. He laid on the floor unconscious with a tube up his cock, completely out of it. When he woke up, he couldn't say a word. And he hasn't spoken a word in ten days. We want you to see if this is some kind of aphasia or if the guy is giving us a fake reaction."

The doctor and two guards then took me to the prison hospital which seemed to be in the middle of the prison's central courtyard. Once again I was reminded of a George Raft movie, as I watched more than twenty prisoners breaking rock boulders with picks and sledge hammers, under the close supervision of several guards. As we walked by the prisoners, several of them directed obscenities my way. The doctor explained to me, "They're looking at you as a brand new queen. This place is divided between kings and queens. The nice guys like doctors, sales guys, or embezzlers are the queens, and tough guys and second-timers are the kings. This Carl guy you're going to see is a decent mannered kind of guy which makes him automatically a queen."

Carl appeared to be in his mid-twenties, mild mannered, and a cooperative man who had been sentenced to prison on an embezzlement conviction. In just a few minutes, I was aware that he understood everything that was said to him. Unlike the responses of a typical aphasic patient, my subsequent testing found that he could read silently, write, and follow spoken instructions with quick, normal ability. His attempts at talking met with total failure. He was even unable to count aloud in a rapid series, which many aphasic patients are able to do. When asked to repeat "ah" after me, he could only posture his mouth with no voice. It became apparent to me that Carl did not have aphasia, but symptoms of an elective mutism. What he needed was a brief exposure to voice therapy with strong psychological support and counseling.

Following my forty-minute examination, I was escorted with the doctor back to the warden's office. As I entered his office, before I could say anything or write my evaluation, the warden asked me, "Does he have aphasia?"

"No, I don't think so," I replied.

Before I could say anything else, the prison doctor interrupted, "It's just what I told you, Warden, there's some kind of hysteria going on here. This guy doesn't have aphasia any more than you do, sir."

The warden's response to my quick answer will always haunt me. He concluded our evaluation by saying, "Well, we'll get that boy to talk. Thank you, Doctor, for confirming what we pretty well knew." Turning to his lieutenant, the warden ordered, "I want that Carl son of a bitch out of the hospital and put on work detail, words or no words."

* * *

I have long wondered whatever happened to Carl after my useless visit. I know that if I had not been trapped into saying a quick "no" to the question, "does he have aphasia?," I could have made a favorable case for Carl. I would have liked to say that many people react to extremes of stress by being unable to speak. Such mutism is not willful or done with deliberation. It is usually a temporary condition of speechlessness which responds well to counseling and psychological support. I wish that I had been able to offer that to Carl.

ARE YOU THE BOYS GOING TO PHILLY?

IT will be difficult to put into words the flight travel experienced by me on an ASHA clinical certification visit to a hospital setting some forty miles west of Philadelphia. A particular body in ASHA, the Professional Services Board (PSB) at the time, asked me and another professional man (Dr. M) to make a visit to a clinical program that had requested PSB renewal certification. To get to the site, I flew from Tucson to Philadelphia, and then took a 90-minute van ride on a shuttle to the visitation city. My visitation colleague, Dr. M had a later but similar 90-minute shuttle ride from Philadelphia to our visitation city.

On the night before our clinic visit, as we were reviewing the submitted program materials, we both agreed that our 90-minute shuttle ride, stopping seemingly at every small town, should be avoided on our return to Philadelphia, if at all possible. After voicing our shuttle complaint to the staff of the speech and hearing clinic, they quickly identified for us a much faster way to return to the Philadelphia airport. There were five or six pilots in town, who collectively owned their own Cessna, and they took turns on particular days to serve as an air taxi service, taking up to three people wherever they needed to go. Our host director called the air service and arranged for both Dr. M and me to fly back to Philadelphia early the next afternoon.

After lunch the next day with our program host, she drove us to the city airport, leaving us with our luggage at a small one-room "terminal." As Dr. M and I waited by the empty building, we became concerned about a possible breakdown in our planned travel. Finally, a large black Chrysler drove up beside us, parking in the adjacent parking area. A tall man got out of the car with some difficulty, and we quickly identified that he had a left-sided hemiplegia. His left arm appeared paralyzed and he walked with what looked like a partially paralyzed left leg, with his foot held up at a right angle by a short leg brace.

He walked with a severe limp towards us and asked, "Are you the boys going to Philly?" Agreeing with his question and attempting to introduce ourselves, he picked up our two cloth pieces of luggage and said to us, "Follow me to that brown and white Cessna parked over there." We followed him, figuring that he hung around the airport collecting monies from passengers, or doing some airport maintenance work, or despite his left sided paralysis of arm and leg, he assisted passengers with their luggage.

He opened the right door of the four-seater Cessna, and he struggled to put our luggage in the storage space behind the two rear seats, and then laughingly added, "We need to put your carry-on cases back with your luggage. We won't have any time for you to do any office work before you get to Philly."

We each had an attaché case which we handed to the airport stranger who placed them back with our luggage. As we stood beside the Cessna, both of us began to feel a bit apprehensive, but particularly Dr. M who had a strong fear of flying.

The airport handyman turned out to be our pilot. He directed Dr. M to sit in the right rear seat and said to me, "I'm going to ask you to fly captain's left chair today. You get up and slide across to the left chair. I'll follow you up and fly right chair."

Both Dr. M and I followed his directions without challenge. Not until we were belted in our respective seats, and until the pilot closed the right door with his normal right hand, did we each appreciate the possible seriousness of our situation. As the pilot slid the right air-vent window open, he said to me, "Loosen that window clip beside you and slide her open. We need a little fresh air in here."

He was obviously aware of our apprehensions and before switching on the engine, gave us some explanations. "You see, I am having trouble moving my left arm. It all started three months ago when I was a victim of a head injury from a total equipment failure. I'll be getting my renewal physical in a couple of months. You have no worry about me flying you to Philly, as I've been flying these birds for over forty years. I'm known in these parts as Captain Bill. The hardest thing I've had to deal with since the crash is getting my feet to work the pedals. As you may know, flying an airplane is all footwork. My left leg now works everything down there fine. My left arm just sits on the yolk but I pull her back or push her down with my right arm. So there's no problem moving the yolk." I could not believe the nightmare Captain Bill was telling us.

"As I told you, I go up for my physical renewal in a couple of months, and in the meantime, I've learned to fly again like any normal guy. They told me you were a couple of speech doctors, and as you hear me talk, I'm sure you'd say I'm a normal talker? We have to be normal talkers, working the radio and all."

I am sure that Dr. M was thinking along with me, "the guy's had head trauma, talks free of dysarthria, doesn't seem to have aphasia or trouble with words, but what about his cognition. Has he lost any of his mechanical abilities or practical intelligence?" Our private thoughts were interrupted as Captain Bill started up the engine.

We immediately began taxiing on the grass beside the paved runway, I thought this was in error and said, "It looks like we're taxiing on the grass. Shouldn't we be moving over on the pavement?"

"No, we never taxi on a runway. We stay on the grass til we reach the end of the runway. We wouldn't want to interfere with incoming traffic landing down on the runway." It was comforting to me to hear his logical explanation.

Captain Bill then explained to me why he had me sit in the left chair, which is usually the chair that the pilot occupies. "I asked you, doctor, to sit in the captain's chair so you could help me with my left arm. When I taxi to the end of the runway, I'd appreciate it if you'd lift my arm up to the yolk so my hand can grab the yolk at the same height as my right hand. When we get enough air speed, I'll pull back on the yolk and we'll lift off the ground. When I tell you to 'pull her down', I'll want you to remove my hand from the yolk and let my arm fall down on my lap. It's most important that you don't touch the yolk, so remember to keep your hand off of the yolk, and just release my hand from the yolk so I can lower my arm down." He repeated the instruction in a loud voice. "When I yell 'UP', lift my left arm up to the yolk. When I yell 'DOWN,' pull her down. That's why you're flying left chair, doctor. Help me with the dead arm." He then asked me to practice a few times the lifting up and the down maneuvers, after which he answered, "Good moves, doctor, just perfect."

I could not believe what Captain Bill had asked me to do. At that point, I believed our "survival" depended on my arm assistance, so I yelled back my confirmation for lifting or lowering his left arm. As he taxied to the end of the runway, he yelled further instructions to both of us, "Once we're airborne, both of you look to the right and to the left, up and down for other air traffic. Let me know what you see!"

At the end of the runway, he revved up his engine for a few minutes. Finally he yelled to me as he released our brakes, "Lift her up!" I lifted his arm to the yolk, and we began increasing our speed down the runway. We were soon airborne, and I followed his instruction to lower his arm from the yolk. With great relief, he pulled back on the yolk with his right arm, and we seemed to have experienced a normal take off. I could hear a very nervous Dr. M in the rear seat let out some low-voice approval.

As we gained altitude, Captain Bill acknowledged both Dr. M's and my warnings about sighting distant aircraft usually saying, "I see him, boys, thanks for the look." The actual flight seemed to be quite routine. I felt that Captain Bill worked the radio and Philadelphia tower instructions with normal procedures, acknowledging the controller's instructions and following them promptly.

As we started our descent into the big Philadelphia airport, Captain Bill was wearing his headphones and spoke in a louder voice to us, "Watch for the big commercial jets that we don't get in their way. I see a big American jumbo coming beside us. They have their own runways and we have our own small one. If you see any of them crossing into our landing space, let me know!"

Just before we touched down, Bill asked me to "Lift her up," and I promptly raised his left arm and hand to the yolk. We landed without any problems, eventually taxiing off to a tarmac used for parking small planes.

As Bill opened the right door and climbed down, stepping down on the wing, he said to us, "Now, that wasn't so bad, was it? It sure as hell must have beat riding all day in that shuttle van they use." He helped me out first and then helped Dr. M step down to the ground. I can well remember how good it felt to be standing on the ground again.

As he took our bags down from the plane, he said to us, "Thanks for flying with us today. The lady at the hospital has already paid for you," Raising his right arm and pointing, "You doctors just follow the arrows and you'll get to the main Philly terminal.

"I'm going to say goodbye to you now 'cause I got to get going back to where we came from." We each said thanks and shook his right hand and he added, "I'll miss you helping me with my left arm, doctor. Whenever I got anyone flying with me since the accident, I always appreciate some extra help to keep things steady."

* * *

Neither Dr. M nor I will ever forget our Cessna flight to Philly. The last time I saw Dr. M at a speech-language pathology convention in Chicago, I asked him with a straight face, "Do you ever hear from Captain Bill?"

EPILOGUE
By Julie B.

IT was a lovely spring day in Tucson, Arizona. My visit to the University of Arizona had been a real pleasure. Every faculty, staff, and student member of the Department of Speech and Hearing Sciences extended the kind of hospitality that made me feel welcome and at home in this strange desert landscape. I completed my presentation to the Department on a positive note and was collecting my presentation materials. Two distinguished looking men approached me and extended their hands to introduce themselves. Tom Shipp and Daniel Boone complimented my presentation and ended by saying, "We really need you here!" These are two men whose work was well known to me through my graduate studies at the University of Iowa. I could not believe my good fortune to meet both of them in person, much less to hear that they wanted me to come to Arizona! In the end, I did accept the offer to join the faculty at the University of Arizona the following year.

Since my arrival in Tucson, Arizona, Dr. Boone has been an important part of my life as a role model, colleague, friend, and laugh therapist. Over lunch and phone conversations, we have shared a love for humor and life stories, many of which Dr. Boone has masterfully written in this clinical narrative in much the same way he might share them in person. As illustrated by these clinical narratives, Dr. Boone has a passion for helping others find their voice, whether their communication impairment is due to a cognitive, motor speech, or voice problem, or psychological response to life's challenges. Dr. Boone never hesitates to reach out to others to help them realize their highest potential, or to promote their best interest. He is also one of the most artful teachers I know. Without the need for hyped up PowerPoint slides or other bells and whistles, Dr. Boone delivers clinical diamonds to my students while their body language conveys that they are hanging on every word. They laugh at his clever wit as Dr. Boone delivers his carefully crafted lesson, complete with self-deprecating punch lines. Every Daniel Boone guest lecture is followed by several student inquiries wondering when the next opportunity to hear from him might be. Dr. Boone's speech-language pathology narrative, **"Damn Shoes and Other Talking Tales"** reminds me of these guest lectures that incorporate case examples showcasing the breadth and depth of his knowledge and skill acquired throughout his esteemed international career as a speech-language pathologist, Professor, ASHA President, author, and other leadership and clinical roles.

Dr. Boone has touched numerous lives and continues to do so to this day. I believe these "talking tales" make an important contribution to our clinical litera-ture and demonstrate the value of our profession across a multitude of settings. One learns about the historical progression of perspectives and approaches to evaluation and management of different communication disorders and their impact on both the patients and the people around them. More importantly, Dr. Boone eloquently portrays the impact of considering the person you treat, rather than seeing someone as a disorder to be treated. I am honored to have the last word in this book that shares numerous treasures in the form of touching, humorous, exemplar, and insightful narratives.....I laughed, I cried. It is clear that Dr. Daniel R. Boone has said much by sharing with the reader a few glimpses at people whose lives he has touched.

Julie Barkmeier-Kraemer, PhD, CCC-SLP
Associate Professor
Department of Speech, Language, Hearing and Sciences
The University of Arizona, Tucson, AZ